CHEM 1110 & CHEM 1120

Author: H. Anthony Neidig, J.N. Spencer

 CENGAGE
Learning·

Australia • Brazil • Japan • Korea • Mexico • Singapore • Spain • United Kingdom • United States

CHEM 1110 & CHEM 1120: ,

Signature Labs
H. Anthony Neidig, J.N. Spencer

© Cengage Learning. All rights reserved.

For product information and technology assistance, contact us at
Cengage Learning Customer & Sales Support, 1-800-354-9706

For permission to use material from this text or product, submit all requests online at **cengage.com/permissions**
Further permissions questions can be emailed to
permissionrequest@cengage.com

This book contains select works from existing Cengage Learning resources and was produced by Cengage Learning Custom Solutions for collegiate use. As such, those adopting and/or contributing to this work are responsible for editorial content accuracy, continuity and completeness.

Compilation © 2016 Cengage Learning

ISBN: 978-1-337-44030-1

Cengage Learning
20 Channel Center Street
Boston, MA 02210
USA

Cengage Learning is a leading provider of customized learning solutions with office locations around the globe, including Singapore, the United Kingdom, Australia, Mexico, Brazil, and Japan. Locate your local office at:
www.international.cengage.com/region.

Cengage Learning products are represented in Canada by Nelson Education, Ltd.

For your lifelong learning solutions, visit **www.cengage.com/custom.**

Visit our corporate website at **www.cengage.com.**

Brief Contents

Table of Contents

Safety Practices in the Chemistry Laboratory

Prepared by H. A. Neidig, Lebanon Valley College, and
J. N. Spencer, Franklin and Marshall College

Safety in the chemistry laboratory depends on a cautious attitude and an awareness of potential hazards. Each person in a laboratory is responsible for the safety of everyone present.

An accident in a chemistry laboratory can cause serious injuries or even death. However, potential hazards can usually be anticipated, thus preventing most accidents. The number of laboratory accidents can be sharply reduced if all safety precautions and directions given for each experiment are strictly followed by every student. Special note should be taken of specific instructions concerning potential hazards. In general, remember these three rules:

- Read the experiment before coming to the laboratory;

- Use common sense when working with laboratory materials and apparatus;

- Know how to get help in case of an accident.

Here are fifteen widely accepted laboratory safety practices:

1. Wear splashproof goggles or glasses at all times, ones that have been approved by the appropriate authorities.

   There is no excuse for injured eyes in a laboratory accident, because adequate eye protection is always available and should always be worn. However, even when goggles are worn, it is recommended that contact lenses not be worn in the laboratory. Even though there is not sufficient evidence to support the position that contact lenses should *never* be worn in the laboratory, it is always possible that a small amount of corrosive material might flow under the edge of a contact lens and cause permanent damage to the eye. Also, contact lenses will hinder immediate and complete flushing of eyes in case a chemical splashes into them.

2. Know the exact location and operation of all safety equipment.

   Your laboratory instructor will identify the location and explain the operation of the eyewash fountain, safety shower, fire alarm, fire blanket, fire extinguisher, fire pail, and emergency exit nearest to your laboratory bench. Learn the locations of this safety equipment and how and when to use it. Your actions during an emergency might prevent a classmate from suffering a serious or fatal injury.

Complete the **Safety Information** section later in this module.

3. *Never* work alone in the laboratory.

A laboratory instructor will always be present during the assigned laboratory period. The instructor will be aware of the exact nature of all work being done in the laboratory. If you encounter any difficulties, the instructor will be available to assist you.

4. Do only the experiment assigned by your laboratory instructor.

Never do an unauthorized experiment in place of the one assigned by your instructor. Do not alter the designated procedure in any way without obtaining permission from your instructor.

5. Wear clothing that will provide the maximum possible protection.

Do not wear open-toed shoes or sandals. You must wear shoes that provide adequate protection from spilled chemicals, broken glass, or apparatus that falls to the floor. Do not wear clothing with loose sleeves. Nonflammable, nonporous laboratory aprons are recommended. All laboratory jackets or coats should have snap closures that can be opened quickly in case of an emergency. Tie back or pin up long hair so that it will neither fall into flames or chemicals nor become entwined in equipment or moving machinery.

6. Place such items as purses, backpacks, sweaters, coats, scarves, and extra books in designated areas, preferably outside the laboratory.

Do not place such items on the laboratory bench or in your working area. Only authorized materials, such as laboratory instructions, a notebook, and a pen or pencils, should be placed on your laboratory bench.

7. Never eat, drink, smoke, chew, or apply lipstick in the laboratory.

In the laboratory, airborne materials and substances spilled on the bench come in direct contact with everything else in the laboratory environment. Thus, if you are working with a toxic substance, it could contaminate any object taken into the laboratory and then later comes in contact with your mouth. To minimize this possibility, never bring food or cigarettes into the laboratory. Do not drink from laboratory glassware, because it might be contaminated with a toxic substance. Because there is a chance that you have a reagent on your hands, keep your hands away from your face and mouth. Wash your hands thoroughly with soap or detergent before leaving the laboratory to avoid any reagent transfer.

8. Dispose of waste materials according to the directions of your laboratory instructor.

Specially marked containers will be provided for such waste materials as broken glass or porcelain-ware, paper, and burned matches. Never throw these materials in the sink or on the floor.

9. Help keep the laboratory clean at all times.

One characteristic of a safe laboratory is that it is clean. Dispose of all materials as directed by your laboratory instructor.

Before you leave the laboratory, wipe the bench top thoroughly. Make certain your work area is clean and free of spilled chemicals, burned matches, and paper scraps.

10. Use a fume hood when you are directed to do so.

   Fume hoods remove toxic vapors and irritating odors from the laboratory. The removal of these materials is essential in order to protect the health and safety of everyone working in the laboratory.

11. Use good judgment and care when working in the laboratory.

   Carefully read the experiment before coming to the laboratory. Know exactly what type of data you should collect from the experiment and how you will use the data. Be sure you understand all cautions about potential hazards and all warnings concerning critical steps in the procedure.

   Do not use glassware that is chipped, cracked, or severely scratched. Replace it with undamaged glassware. Be sure that all glass tubing or rods have been adequately firepolished.

   Be very careful when inserting glass tubing, glass rods, thermometers, funnels, or thistle tubes into rubber stoppers or corks. Protect your hands by holding the glass and stopper with a cloth towel or multiple layers of paper towelling (see Figure 1). Always lubricate the glass surface with water or glycerine before inserting the glassware into a stopper or cork.

   Never deliberately taste any chemical in the laboratory.

   Avoid inhaling fumes of any kind. In case you do need to detect an odor in an experiment, gently waft the vapors toward your nose with a cupped hand, as shown in Figure 2, or use the method recommended by your laboratory instructor. *Never* put your face directly over a container, such as a test tube, and directly inhale vapors.

   Inform your instructor at the first laboratory session if you have a particular allergy or medical condition. This information is necessary for your own safety as well as for that of everyone working around you.

12. Avoid touching hot objects.

   Remember that when you heat a chemical in a container, the burner or hot plate *and* the clamp holding the container also get hot.

   Do not lay hot glass tubing directly on the laboratory bench or on a towel. Instead, place the tubing on a piece of heat-resistant board. You can use a "Hot Object" sign to warn others and help them avoid injury.

13. Read the labels on reagent bottles and containers to make certain that they contain the appropriate chemicals for the experiment.

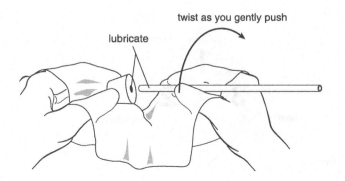

twist as you gently push

lubricate

Figure 1

Inserting glass tubing into a stopper

Figure 2
Detecting odors

Before removing a chemical or solution from a reagent bottle, read the label carefully. Make certain that you have the desired reagent. Record the identity of the reagent and, if appropriate, its concentration on your data sheet or in your notebook. To ensure accurate identification of the reagent, read the label again before putting the container back on the shelf.

Note whether or not the National Fire Protection Association (NFPA) diamond-shaped hazard rating label has been applied to the reagent container. This label, shown in Figure 3, lists the NFPA hazard ratings [(0–4) from least to most hazardous] for the substance in the bottle and the personal protection required when using the reagent.

Material safety data sheets (MSDS) for all the hazardous chemicals used are on file at the site in which the chemical is used. Federal law requires that the information on the sheets be made available to users of these chemicals by the chemical supplier. The first section of an MSDS usually lists all the names by which the chemical is known, its chemical formula, supplier's name, and, when appropriate, the NFPA hazard ratings. The remaining sections may include such information as ingredients and hazards; physical data; fire and explosion data; reactivity data; health hazard information; spill, leak, and disposal procedures; special protection information; and special precautions and comments.

MSDS vary from one supplier to another in terms of their layout and exact contents. Part of a typical MSDS for acetone is shown in Figure 4 on the next page.

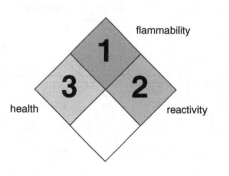

Figure 3
A typical NFPA hazard label

MATERIAL SAFETY DATA SHEET

Section 1. IDENTITY

Name	**ACETONE**	NFPA Hazard Rating	
Synonyms	**2-PROPANONE, DIMETHYLKETONE**	health	1
Formula	$CH_3C(O)CH_3$	flammability	3
RTECS No.	**AL3150000**	reactivity	0
CAS No.	**67-64-1**		

Section 2. HAZARDOUS COMPONENTS

Component	%	TLV
ACETONE	100	1000 ppm (2375 mg/m^3)

Section 3. PHYSICAL DATA

Clear, colorless, volatile liquid with a characteristic mint-like odor. Soluble in alcohol, ether, benzene, chloroform, most dimethylformamides, and oils.

Boiling point: 133 °F (56 °C). Specific Gravity: 0.7899.
Volatility: 100%. Vapor pressure: 180 mm Hg @ 20 °C.

Section 4. FIRE, EXPLOSION HAZARDS

Dangerous fire hazard when exposed to heat or flame. Vapors are heavier than air and may travel a considerable distance to source of ignition.

Flash point: −4 °F (−20 °C).

Section 5. HEALTH HAZARDS

Inhalation: Irritant and narcotic. 20,000 ppm immediately dangerous to life.

Section 6. STORAGE AND HANDLING

Observe all federal, state, and local regulations when storing or disposing of this substance. For assistance, contact the district director of the Environmental Protection Agency.
STORAGE: Store in accordance with 29 CFR 1910.106. Bonding and grounding: Substance with low electro-conductivity that may be ignited by electrostatic sparks should be stored in containers that meet the bonding and grounding guidelines specified in NFPA 77-1983. Store away from incompatible substances.

Section 7. SPILLS AND DISPOSAL

Disposal must be in accordance with standards applicable to generators of hazardous waste; see 40 CFR 262. EPA hazardous waste number U002. Occupational spill: Shut off ignition sources. Stop leak if you can do so without risk. Use water spray to reduce vapors. For small spills, take up with sand or other absorbent material, and place into containers for later disposal.

Figure 4
Partial MSDS for acetone showing typical format

14. Wash your hands thoroughly before leaving the laboratory.

    Before you leave the laboratory, wash your hands thoroughly with soap or detergent and warm water to remove all traces of reagents from your skin. Be careful to avoid transferring reagents to your mouth, eyes, face, or other parts of your body.

15. Immediately report all physical and chemical injuries to your laboratory instructor, no matter how minor the injury might seem.

IF AN ACCIDENT OCCURS . . .

In spite of the best efforts of all concerned, laboratory accidents do occur. Consequently, you must know what to do in particular situations.

The following examples illustrate some of the more common accidents. Your laboratory instructor will elaborate on the general information presented here. Your instructor will suggest modifications of this information that might be more appropriate for possible situations in your laboratory.

Immediately report all accidents and injuries, however minor, to your laboratory instructor.

Chemical Spills on the Laboratory Bench, Reagent Shelf, or Floor

Immediately notify your bench neighbors and your laboratory instructor about the spill and the substances involved. If the spill involves volatile, flammable materials, tell everyone in the laboratory to extinguish all flames. Disconnect any spark-producing equipment. Shut down all experiments. Evacuate the laboratory, if your laboratory instructor tells you to do so.

Chemical Spills on a Person

Over a Large Area

Immediately notify your laboratory instructor, who might take one or both of the following actions, depending on the extent and location of the spill:

Quickly remove all contaminated clothing while the person is under the safety shower. Flood the affected body area with cold water for at least 15 minutes.

Wash off chemicals with a mild detergent solution. Do not apply any other materials to the area. Rinse the affected area with cold water. Obtain medical assistance immediately.

Over a Small Area

Immediately flush the area thoroughly with cold water. Notify your laboratory instructor, who will take appropriate further action.

In the Eyes

If chemicals do happen to splash into your eyes, immediate attention is critical. Immediately call for assistance in getting to the eyewash fountain.

Drench your eyes for at least 20 minutes. Carefully force your eyes wide open in order to get water into them. Rotate your eyeballs in order to flush all areas.

Your laboratory instructor will make the necessary arrangements for you to obtain medical assistance.

If a chemical splashes on your face while you are wearing splashproof goggles or glasses, *KEEP THE GOGGLES ON*. If you remove the goggles immediately following such a spill, the splashed chemical may get into your eyes.

Immediately call for assistance in getting to the nearest eyewash fountain, where you should drench your face and goggles. When you have removed all of the chemical from your face and goggles, take off the goggles.

Ingestion of Chemicals

Notify your laboratory instructor immediately. Your instructor will take action that is appropriate for the specific substance ingested.

Burns

Immediately notify your laboratory instructor of any burn. Burns from hot objects, flames, or chemicals should all be treated in the same way: Flush the affected area with cool, running water for 20 minutes. Your instructor will determine whether or not the burn should receive medical attention.

Cuts and Wounds

Any cut or wound in the laboratory must be considered serious and treated carefully. Immediately notify your laboratory instructor. Your instructor will determine what kind of medical attention is needed. Avoid contaminating any materials used to treat the wound with laboratory reagents.

Unconsciousness

Either electric shock or inhalation of or skin contact with certain chemicals can cause respiratory failure and unconsciousness. If anyone becomes unconscious in the laboratory, immediately call for your laboratory instructor.

Fire

The procedure most often recommended in cases in which an individual's clothing is burning is called *STOP-DROP-ROLL: STOP* what you are doing; *DROP* to the floor; *ROLL* over and over again to extinguish the flames.

If your clothing starts burning, move away from the source of the fire. Call for help. *STOP-DROP-ROLL* until someone else gets a fire blanket to help smother the flames on your clothing.

Do not run to the fire blanket or safety shower. Running increases the burning rate and accelerates the inhalation of hot, toxic fumes, thus increasing chances of respiratory damage.

If someone else's clothing catches fire, move the person away from the source of the fire. Make them *STOP-DROP-ROLL*. Use the fire blanket to help smother the flames on the clothing. Immediately call for your laboratory instructor.

You should remove the fire blanket as soon as the flames have been extinguished, so that the victim will not be burned further by hot clothing. Your laboratory instructor may place the victim in the safety shower at this point.

While the victim is being cared for, other people should try to shut off or reduce the fuel supply to the source of the fire. Try to control and extinguish the fire by directing the spray of an appropriate fire extinguisher at the fire base.

Alert the proper authorities about the fire and its status. Call for additional assistance if needed.

Carefully read the **Chemistry Laboratory Safety Agreement** found in this module. The agreement requires both your signature and that of your laboratory instructor.

Safety Information

The safety information presented here applies to any chemistry laboratory. Therefore, you should be thoroughly familiar with it. Many experiments contain additional warnings about steps that may be dangerous. For this reason it is important that you read the entire experiment before attempting to carry out the procedure.

Be especially aware of the safety information for your laboratory. Following are the names of safety equipment and facilities usually found in a typical chemistry laboratory. Next to each name, write the location of that item in your laboratory. There is also space for important telephone numbers and additional safety instructions that your laboratory instructor may give you. In an emergency, this information will help you to quickly take the correct action. A few seconds saved can mean the difference between severe injury or damage and a minor inconvenience.

When you have completed all the information, ask your laboratory instructor to sign and date your copy. Retain this information for your use.

shower: **fire exits:**

eyewash fountains: **fire extinguishers:**

first-aid station: **fire blankets:**

material safety data sheets: **nearest telephone:**

emergency telephone numbers:

fire: **poison center:**   **police:**

additional safety instructions:

_____   _____

laboratory instructor's signature   *date*

Chemistry Laboratory Safety Agreement

Anytime I am working in or visiting the laboratory, I will follow the laboratory safety practices recommended in this module and take the following precautions:

1. Wear splashproof goggles or glasses at all times.
2. Know the exact location and operation of all safety equipment.
3. Never work alone in the laboratory.
4. Do only the experiment assigned by my laboratory instructor.
5. Wear clothing that will provide the maximum possible protection.
6. Place such things as purses, backpacks, sweaters, coats, scarves, and extra books in designated areas, preferably outside the laboratory.
7. Never eat, drink, smoke, chew, or apply lipstick in the laboratory.
8. Dispose of waste materials according to the directions of my laboratory instructor.
9. Help keep the laboratory clean at all times.
10. Use a fume hood when directed to do so.
11. Use good judgment and care when working in the laboratory.
12. Avoid touching hot objects.
13. Read the labels on reagent bottles and containers to make certain that they contain the appropriate chemicals for the experiment.
14. Wash my hands thoroughly before leaving the laboratory.
15. Immediately report all physical and chemical injuries to my laboratory instructor, no matter how minor the injury seems.

I have carefully read the discussion of recommended laboratory safety practices and the precautions listed above. I understand their importance in preserving the safety of everyone in the laboratory.

I recognize my responsibility to follow these practices and precautions while I am present in the laboratory.

_____   _____
student's signature   date

_____   _____
course   laboratory section

_____   _____
laboratory locker number   room number

_____   _____
laboratory instructor's signature   date

_____   _____   _____
name   *section*   *date*

Laboratory Safety Quiz

1. When should splashproof goggles or glasses be worn in the laboratory?

2. Under what conditions is it permissible to work alone in the laboratory?

3. What is the purpose of a fume hood?

4. If a chemical spill occurs, what immediate action should you take?

5. If a chemical splashes into your eyes, what should you do?

6. Describe three steps to take that will sharply reduce the number of laboratory accidents.

7. List safety violations made by Sarah in the following situation.

Sarah walked into the laboratory and began reading the day's experiment for the first time. She found her safety goggles too hot and cumbersome, so she removed them when she was not handling reagents. Sarah noticed a red solid in a reagent bottle on the side shelf. "I wonder what would happen if I heated some of this solid in a test tube," she thought. She put on her goggles and poured some of the red solid into a test tube, ignited the gas from her burner, threw the burning match into the sink, and began to heat the solid. As the solid was heating, a brownish-red vapor formed, which produced an unpleasant sensation when Sarah smelled it, startling her. At that point, her loose-sleeved blouse brushed the burner flame and caught fire. Sarah screamed, threw the test tube with the red solid on the floor, and ran from the laboratory.

Common Equipment

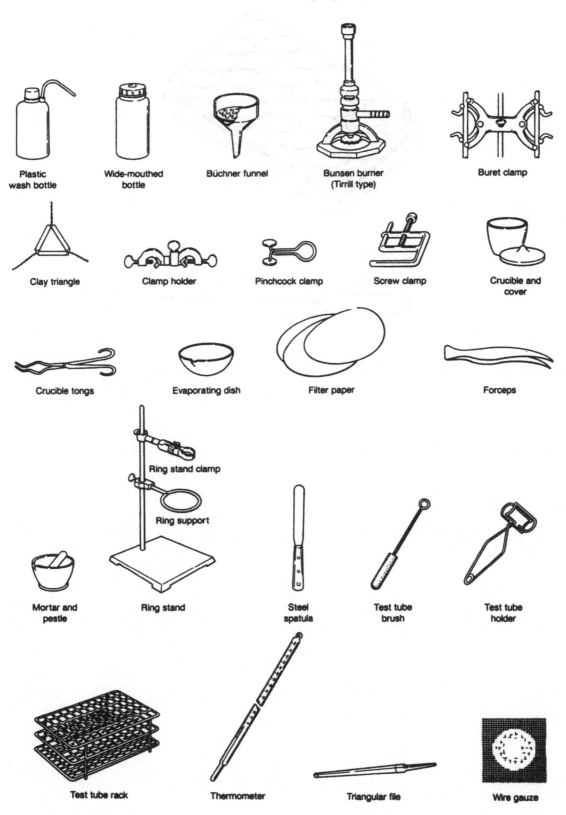

Plastic wash bottle

Wide-mouthed bottle

Büchner funnel

Bunsen burner (Tirrill type)

Buret clamp

Clay triangle

Clamp holder

Pinchcock clamp

Screw clamp

Crucible and cover

Crucible tongs

Evaporating dish

Filter paper

Forceps

Ring stand clamp

Ring support

Mortar and pestle

Ring stand

Steel spatula

Test tube brush

Test tube holder

Test tube rack

Thermometer

Triangular file

Wire gauze

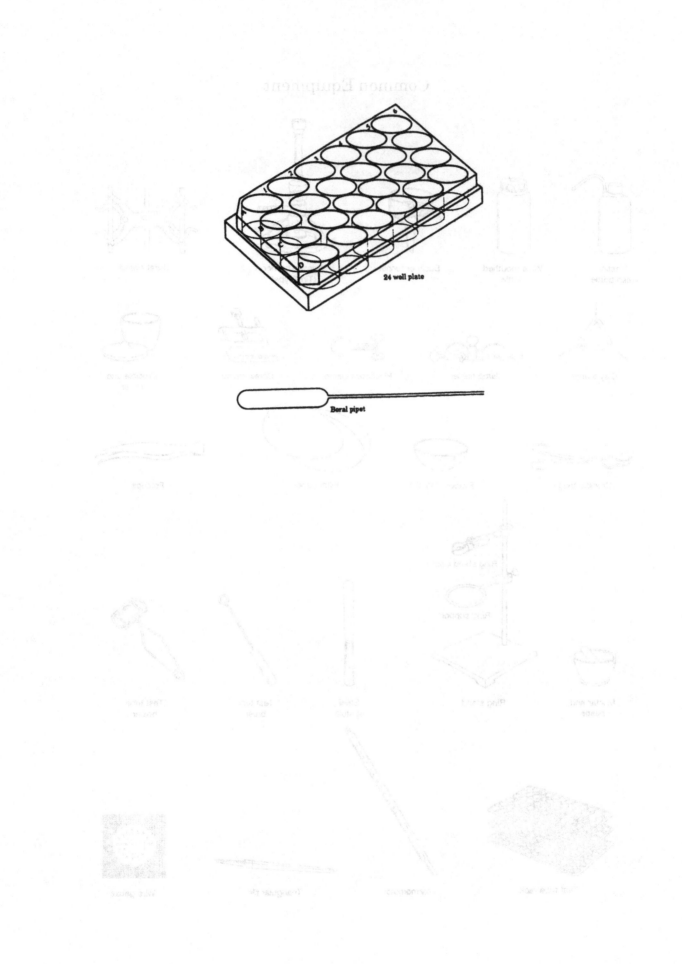

24 well plate

Beral pipet

Isolating the Components of a Three-Component Mixture

Prepared by H. A. Neidig, J. Iskowitz, and M. Royer, Lebanon Valley College, and M. L. Gillette, Indiana University Kokomo

PURPOSE OF THE EXPERIMENT

Separate the components of a mixture of sand, sodium chloride, and calcium carbonate. Calculate the percent, by mass, of each component in the original mixture. Calculate the percent recovery of all components.

BACKGROUND REQUIRED

You should understand the concepts associated with physical and chemical properties of substances, and how to interpret chemical equations.

BACKGROUND INFORMATION

To isolate the components of a mixture, we take advantage of differences among the physical and chemical properties of the individual components. Examples of **physical properties** are solubility and boiling point. **Chemical properties** include reactivity and bond type.

Separation processes based on physical differences in components, called **physical methods**, include:

- **decantation**, the separation of a liquid from a solid by careful pouring. In this process, we allow the solid to settle to the bottom of the container. Then we pour the liquid, which is called the **supernatant liquid** or **supernate**, from the vessel without disturbing the solid.

- **filtration**, the separation of a solid from a liquid by passing the liquid through a porous material, such as filter paper. The solid remaining behind on the paper is called the **residue**. The liquid that passes through the paper is called the **filtrate**.

- **evaporation**, the separation of a solvent from a solution by heating. The remaining residue is the substance that had been dissolved in the solvent.

- **extraction**, which is a separation process we can use when only one component of a mixture is soluble in a specific added solvent. After adding the solvent, we can recover the insoluble component(s) by removing the solvent, using decantation or filtration.

    On the other hand, **chemical methods** of separation involve the chemical conversion of one (or more) mixture component into a different substance, one with physical properties that we can utilize for its separation. Once we have separated the substance, we perform a second reaction to return the substance to its original form.

Example

Problem Separate the components of a water-insoluble mixture of barium sulfate ($BaSO_4$) and nickel(II) carbonate ($NiCO_3$). Indicate the rationale for each separation step. Write chemical equations for all observed reactions.

Solution **(1)** *Add 3M hydrochloric acid (HCl) to the mixture.*
$BaSO_4$ is unaffected. $NiCO_3$ reacts as shown in Equation 1.

$$NiCO_3(s) + 2\,HCL(aq) \rightarrow NiCl_2(aq) + CO_2(g) + H_2O(l) \qquad \text{(Eq. 1)}$$

(2) *Recover the $BaSO_4$.*
Separate the solid $BaSO_4$ using filtration. Dry the $BaSO_4$.

(3) *Convert the $NiCl_2(aq)$ back to $NiCO_3(s)$.*
Add potassium carbonate (K_2CO_3) solution to the filtrate. K_2CO_3 reacts with $NiCl_2(aq)$ as shown in Equation 2.

$$NiCl_2(aq) + K_2CO_3(aq) \rightarrow NiCO_3(s) + 2\,KCl(aq) \qquad \text{(Eq. 2)}$$

(4) *Recover the $NiCO_3$.*
Filter the solid $NiCO_3$ from the solution. Dry the solid.

In This Experiment

You will use the four physical methods previously described, plus one chemical method, to separate and isolate the components of a mixture of sand (SiO_2), sodium chloride (NaCl), and calcium carbonate ($CaCO_3$). Then you will calculate the percent by mass of each component in the original mixture and the percent recovery of all components.

Table 1 *Selected physical and chemical properties of several common compounds*

compound	physical soluble in H_2O	chemical reacts with 3M HCl
$BaSO_4$	no	no
$NiCO_3$	no	yes
SiO_2	no	no
NaCl	yes	no
$CaCO_3$	no	yes
$CaSO_4$	no	no
$Ca(NO_3)_2$	yes	no

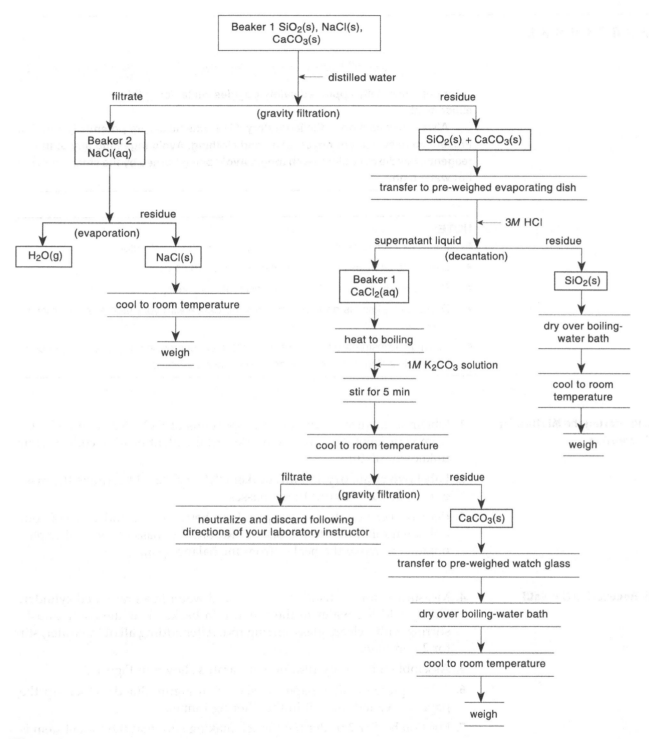

Figure 1

Flowchart for the separation of a mixture of SiO₂, NaCl, and CaCO₃

One physical and one chemical property of each of these substances are listed in Table 1.

In Figure 1, a flowchart is used to summarize the procedural steps you will follow. A **flowchart** is a diagram representing a series of operations.

PROCEDURE

> **CAUTION**
>
> Wear departmentally approved safety goggles while doing this experiment.
>
> Always use caution in the laboratory. Many chemicals are potentially harmful. Prevent contact with your eyes, skin, and clothing. Avoid ingesting any of the reagents. Handle hot objects with tongs. Avoid being burned by the steam from the hot-water bath.

NOTE:

- Label your equipment as directed by your laboratory instructor.
- Determine all masses to the nearest centigram (0.01 g).
- Record all data on your Data and Observations sheet.
- Dispose of all solids and solutions in accordance with your laboratory instructor's directions.
- You may be instructed to complete the entire experiment in one laboratory period or to complete Part IV during a subsequent laboratory period.

I. Preparing the Mixture for Separation

1. Obtain a mixture of unknown proportions of SiO_2, NaCl, and $CaCO_3$ from your laboratory instructor. Record the identification code of your unknown mixture.

2. Label two clean, dry 150-mL beakers "1" and "2". Determine the mass of each beaker. Record these masses.

3. Place beaker 1 on the balance pan. Pour between 2.50 and 3.00 g of your unknown mixture into the beaker. Record the mass of the beaker plus mixture. Remove the beaker from the balance pan.

II. Recovering the NaCl

Figure 2
A gravity filtration assembly

4. Measure 50 mL of distilled or deionized water in a graduated cylinder. Slowly add the water to the mixture in beaker 1, while continuously stirring with a clean, glass stirring rod. After adding all of the water, stir for 2 min more.

5. Assemble the gravity filtration apparatus shown in Figure 2.

6. Fold a piece of filter paper as shown in Figure 3(a–d). Open up the paper cone, and place it in the filtering funnel.

7. Position beaker 2 under the funnel, making sure that the funnel stem is touching the inside wall of the beaker, as shown in Figure 2. Pour as much of the supernatant liquid as possible from beaker 1 into the funnel. Collect the filtrate in beaker 2.

8. Transfer the solid remaining in beaker 1 into the funnel, using a stream of distilled water from a wash bottle, as shown in Figure 4. Use a stirring rod fitted with a rubber policeman to transfer any remaining solid into the funnel. Then rinse the rubber policeman with a stream of distilled water from the wash bottle, allowing the rinses to go into the funnel.

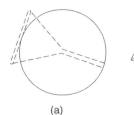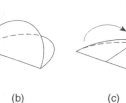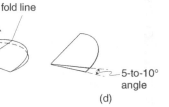

5-to-10°
angle

(a)   (b)   (c)   (d)

Figure 3
Folding a piece of filter paper

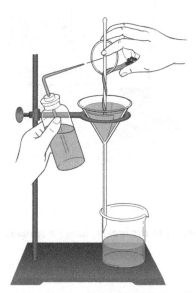

Figure 4
Transferring a solid from a beaker to a filtering funnel

CAUTION

As the volume of the heated solution decreases in Step 9, the risk of splattering increases. Gentle heating and attentiveness will reduce this risk.

---

9. Place beaker 2, containing the filtrate, on a hot plate set on "high". Stabilize the beaker using your support ring, as shown in Figure 5(a) on the next page. Heat the solution to boiling. Then reduce the hot plate setting so that the solution continues to boil gently. Allow it to boil until all of the liquid has evaporated.

   As soon as the water has evaporated, use beaker tongs to move the beaker from the hot plate to a heat-resistant mat, as shown in Figure 5(b) on the next page. Turn off the hot plate. Allow the beaker and its contents to cool to room temperature. While the beaker is cooling, perform Steps 11 and 12.

10. Determine the mass of beaker 2 plus NaCl. Record this mass. Then, discard the NaCl as directed.

    Wash beakers 1 and 2. Rinse each beaker twice with distilled water. Dry beaker 1 for use in Part III. Rinse the glass stirring rod.

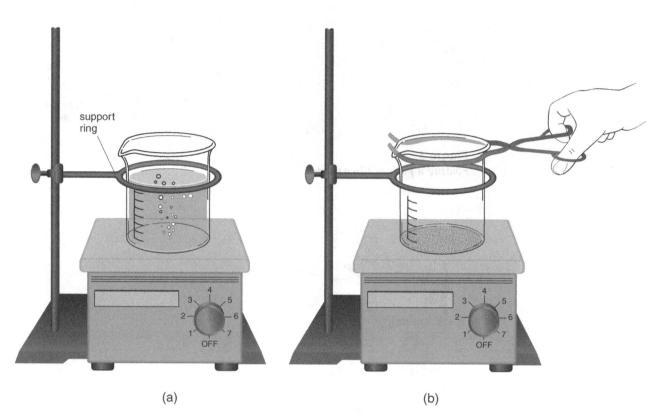

(a)   (b)

Figure 5
Using a hot plate to heat a liquid in a beaker: (a) stabilizing the beaker, using a support ring; (b) removing a hot beaker, using beaker tongs

III. Recovering the SiO₂

11. Determine the mass of a clean, dry evaporating dish. Record this mass.

12. Carefully remove the filter paper and residue from the funnel. Place the paper and residue on your pre-weighed evaporating dish. Open up the filter paper.

    Carefully wash all of the residue from the filter paper into the evaporating dish, using about 5 mL of distilled water from a wash bottle. Discard the filter paper as directed.

    Without losing any residue, decant as much water as possible from the evaporating dish into a clean 100-mL beaker. Pour the water from the beaker into the drain.

CAUTION	⚠

Hydrogen chloride is a corrosive, toxic substance that can cause burns.

NOTE: In Step 13, add the acid *slowly* to control the rate of evolution of CO₂ gas. Release of large amounts of CO₂ could cause a loss of SiO₂ and CaCO₃.

---

13. Measure 8 mL of 3*M* HCl in a clean, dry graduated cylinder. Slowly add the acid to the residue in the evaporating dish. Stir the solution with a clean, glass stirring rod until there is no longer any evidence of gas evolution.

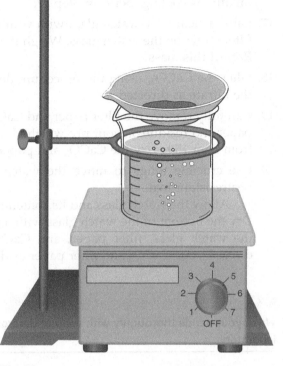

Figure 6
Drying a solid in an evaporating dish

14. Decant as much of the supernatant liquid as possible from the evaporating dish into beaker 1.

    Rinse the residue in the evaporating dish with about 5 mL of distilled water. Allow the solid to settle to the bottom of the dish. Decant the rinses into beaker 1. Repeat the rinsing procedure twice more, each time decanting the rinses into beaker 1. Save the contents of beaker 1 for use in Step 16.

15. Dry the SiO_2 by placing the evaporating dish on top of a 400-mL beaker of water on a hot plate, as shown in Figure 6. Heat the water to boiling, and continue heating until the SiO_2 is completely dry.

    Use crucible tongs to transfer the hot evaporating dish to a heat-resistant mat. Turn off the hot plate. Allow the dish and its contents to cool to room temperature.

    Unless you have been instructed to perform Part IV during your next laboratory period, begin Step 16 while the dish and contents are cooling.

    Once the dish has cooled, dry the bottom with a clean towel. Determine the mass of the dish plus SiO_2. Record this mass. Then, discard the SiO_2 as directed.

IV. Recovering the $CaCO_3$

16. Place beaker 1, containing the supernatant liquid and rinses from Step 14, on a hot plate, using the setup shown in Figure 5(a). Heat to boiling. Allow the solution to boil for 5 min. Then, use beaker tongs to move the beaker from the hot plate (see Figure 5(b)) to a heat-resistant mat. Immediately add 15 mL of $1M$ K_2CO_3. Stir the reaction mixture for

5 min. Allow the mixture to cool to room temperature. While the mixture is cooling, perform Step 17.

17. Label a clean, dry watch glass with your initials. Place a clean piece of filter paper on the watch glass. Weigh the watch glass plus filter paper. Record this mass.

18. Filter the $CaCO_3$, using the procedure described in Steps 5–8. Discard the filtrate as directed.

19. Carefully remove the filter paper and $CaCO_3$ from the funnel. Place the paper and residue on your pre-weighed watch glass. Use the procedure from Step 15 to dry the $CaCO_3$ and paper (see Figure 6).

20. Use crucible tongs to move the watch glass and its contents to a heatresistant mat.

    Allow the watch glass and its contents to cool to room temperature. Dry the bottom of the watch glass with a towel. Determine the mass of the watch glass, filter paper, and $CaCO_3$. Record this mass. Then, discard your $CaCO_3$ and filter paper as directed.

CAUTION

Wash your hands thoroughly with soap or detergent before leaving the laboratory.

_____   _____   _____   _____
Name   *Partner*   *Section*   *Date*

Post-Laboratory Questions

Use the spaces provided for the answers and additional paper if necessary.

1. In the Procedure for this experiment, you used four different physical separation methods. Complete (a)–(d) below, listing the four methods and briefly describing one example of the use of each in this experiment. Include the number of the step in which you used the method.

  (a) Separation method:

      Use in this experiment:

  (b) Separation method:

      Use in this experiment:

  (c) Separation method:

      Use in this experiment:

  (d) Separation method:

      Use in this experiment:

2. In the Procedure for this experiment, you used one chemical separation method. Identify the steps in which you used this method, and describe the process involved.

3. Consider your calculated percent recovery of all components.

   (a) Was your percent recovery greater than, or less than, 100%?

   (b) If your percent recovery was greater than 100%, suggest an explanation. If your percent recovery was less than 100%, which component do you think was recovered least efficiently? Briefly explain.

_____   _____   _____   _____
Name   *Partner*   *Section*   *Date*

Data and Observations

I. Preparing the Mixture for Separation

identification code of unknown mixture   _____

mass of beaker 1, g   _____

mass of beaker 2, g   _____

mass of beaker 1 plus mixture, g   _____

II. Recovering the NaCl

mass of beaker 2 plus NaCl, g   _____

III. Recovering the SiO$_2$

mass of evaporating dish, g   _____

mass of evaporating dish plus SiO$_2$, g   _____

IV. Recovering the CaCO$_3$

mass of watch glass plus filter paper, g   _____

mass of watch glass, filter paper, and CaCO$_3$, g   _____

Calculations and Conclusions

Show your calculations in the space provided. Remember to include units with all calculated results.

I. Preparing the Mixture for Separation

1. Calculate the mass of unknown mixture you analyzed.

II. Recovering the NaCl

2. Calculate the mass of NaCl recovered.

3. Calculate the percent NaCl in your unknown mixture, using Equation 3.

$$\text{percent NaCl in the mixture, } \% = \left(\frac{\text{mass of NaCl recovered, g}}{\text{mass of sample analyzed, g}} \right)(100\%) \qquad \text{(Eq. 3)}$$

III. Recovering the SiO$_2$

4. Calculate the mass of SiO$_2$ recovered.

5. Calculate the percent SiO$_2$ in your unknown mixture, using a modification of Equation 3.

IV. Recovering the CaCO₃

6. Calculate the mass of $CaCO_3$ recovered.

7. Calculate the percent $CaCO_3$ in your unknown mixture, using a modification of Equation 3.

8. Calculate the percent recovery of all mixture components, using Equation 4.

$$\text{percent recovery, \% } = \left(\frac{\text{total mass of recovered NaCl, SiO}_2\text{, and CaCO}_3\text{, g}}{\text{mass of sample analyzed, g}}\right)(100\%) \qquad \text{(Eq. 4)}$$

9. Calculate the percent error for your recovery of the mixture components, using Equation 5.

$$\text{percent error, \%}$$
$$= \left(\frac{\text{mass of sample analyzed, g} - \text{total mass of recovered NaCl, SiO}_2\text{, and CaCO}_3\text{, g}}{\text{mass of sample analyzed, g}}\right)(100\%)$$
$$\text{(Eq. 5)}$$

_____   _____   _____   _____
Name   *Partner*   *Section*   *Date*

Pre-Laboratory Assignment

1. What hazard(s) should you be aware of when drying your recovered SiO_2 and $CaCO_3$? Briefly explain.

2. Define the following terms as they pertain to this experiment.

    (a) supernatant liquid

    (b) filtrate

    (c) residue

3. Briefly explain the following precautions:

    (a) In Step 13, you should add the $3M$ HCl slowly.

    (b) In Step 20, you should completely dry the bottom of the watch glass before weighing the watch glass and its contents.

4. A student separated a 2.13-g sample of the $BaSO_4$/$NiCO_3$ mixture described in the Example in the Background Information section. He recovered 1.02 g $BaSO_4$ and 0.81 g $NiCO_3$.

   (a) Calculate the percent recovery of both components.

   (b) Calculate the percent error for the student's recovery.

PROP **0515**

Using Density to Determine the Sugar Content in Commercial Beverages

Prepared by S. K. Henderson, C. A. Fenn, and J. D. Domijan, Quinnipiac College

PURPOSE OF THE EXPERIMENT

Measure densities of solutions with known sugar content. Prepare a graph relating density to sugar content. Determine densities and corresponding sugar contents of various commercial beverages.

BACKGROUND REQUIRED

You should be familiar with techniques for measuring mass and volume, and for calculating density. You should also be familiar with graphing techniques, either manual or computerized.

BACKGROUND INFORMATION

We define **density** as the ratio of a substance's mass to its volume, as shown in Equation 1.

$$\text{denstiy, g/mL} = \frac{\text{mass, g}}{\text{volume, mL}} \qquad \text{(Eq. 1)}$$

We can use Equation 1 to calculate a solution's density, once we have measured the mass of a known volume of the solution.

Suppose we prepare a solution by dissolving sugar in water. The solution's density depends on how much sugar we dissolve in the water. As we increase the solution's sugar content, the solution's density also increases.

In order to determine the exact relationship between a solution's density and sugar content, we first prepare solutions with known sugar content. We express the sugar content in terms of **mass percent**, as defined by Equation 2.

$$\text{mass percent sugar, \%} = \left(\frac{\text{mass of sugar}}{\text{mass of solution}} \right) (100\%) \qquad \text{(Eq. 2)}$$

We then determine the densities of these solutions. On a graph, we plot each solution's density on the y-axis and its mass percent sugar on the x-axis. The resulting graph is a straight line with positive slope.

If we then determine the density of a commercial beverage, we can use this graph to determine the mass percent sugar in the beverage. Water and sugar are the major components of beverages such as fruit juices, iced tea, lemonade, and sodas. Other ingredients, such as flavorings, do not contribute measurably to these beverages' densities.

Example

Problem 1 Suppose a student prepares a solution of sodium chloride (NaCl) in water. The student dissolves 1.05 g of NaCl in about 50 mL of water. The mass of the final solution is 51.98 g. Determine the mass percent NaCl in the solution.

Solution We adapt Equation 2 to show NaCl in water.

$$\text{mass percent NaCl, }\% = \left(\frac{\text{mass of NaCl}}{\text{mass of solution}}\right)(100\%) = \left(\frac{1.05\,\text{g}}{51.98\,\text{g}}\right)(100\%) = 2.02\%$$

Problem 2 The student uses a pipet to transfer 10.00 mL of the NaCl solution to a beaker. The student determines that the mass of this volume of solution is 10.08 g. Calculate the density of the solution.

Solution We use Equation 1.

$$\text{density, g/mL} = \frac{\text{mass, g}}{\text{volume, mL}} = \left(\frac{10.08\,\text{g}}{10.00\,\text{mL}}\right) = 1.008\,\text{g/mL}$$

Problem 3 The student prepares two other NaCl–H_2O solutions. The student determines the densities of these solutions, as well as that of distilled water. The student's results are compiled in the following table.

	water	*solution* 1	2	3
mass percent NaCl, %	0	2.02	4.07	6.16
density, g/mL	0.993	1.008	1.021	1.034

Prepare a graph of density versus NaCl content for these solutions, and use it to determine the relationship between density and NaCl concentration.

Solution We plot density on the y-axis and mass percent NaCl on the x-axis, as shown in Figure 1. We then draw the best straight line through these points.

If we determine the trend line for these data via regression analysis, using a software spreadsheet, we find that:

$$\text{density, g/mL} = (0.0066\,\text{g/mL}\cdot\%)(\text{mass percent NaCl}) + 0.994\,\text{g/mL}$$

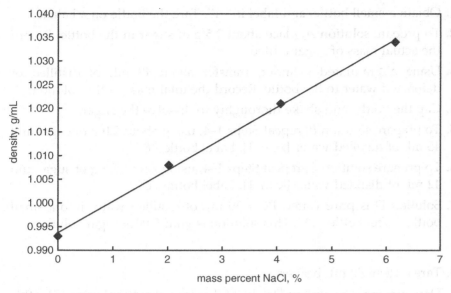

Figure 1
Plot of student-prepared NaCl solution concentrations and corresponding densities

Problem 4 The student obtains an unknown NaCl–H_2O sample and determines that its density is 1.015 g/mL. Determine the mass percent NaCl in this sample.

Solution We locate the density of 1.015 g/mL on the y-axis of the graph in Problem 3. We position a ruler horizontally at that point on the y-axis, and note where it intersects the straight line graph. We then drop the ruler vertically from the intersection point to the x-axis. We read the mass percent NaCl on the x-axis, which appears to be 3.2%.

Alternatively, we substitute the solution's density into the straight-line equation relating density to mass percent NaCl, as determined in Problem 3.

$$1.015 \text{ g/mL} = (0.0066 \text{ g/mL} \cdot \%)(\text{mass percent NaCl}) + 0.994 \text{ g/mL}$$

$$\text{mass percent NaCl, } \% = \frac{(1.015 \text{ g/mL} - 0.994 \text{ g/mL})}{0.0066 \text{ g/mL} \cdot \%} = 3.2\%$$

PROCEDURE

CAUTION

Wear departmentally approved safety goggles while doing this experiment.
Avoid ingesting all solids and solutions used in the laboratory. Never drink from laboratory glassware, because of possible contamination.

NOTE: Record all measurements on your Data Sheet. Record all masses to either the nearest milligram (0.001 g) or the nearest centigram (0.01 g), as indicated by your laboratory instructor.

I. Preparing Solutions of Known Sugar Content

1. Obtain a small bottle, and label it "A". Tare the bottle on a balance.

2. To prepare solution A, place about 2.5 g of sugar in the bottle. Record the actual mass of sugar added.

3. Using a graduated cylinder, transfer about 48 mL of distilled or deionized water to the bottle. Record the total mass of the solution.

4. Cap the bottle, and shake thoroughly to dissolve the sugar.

NOTE 1: Record the actual mass of sugar added and the total mass of solution for solutions B and C.

5. To prepare solution B, repeat Steps 1–4, using about 5.0 g of sugar and 45 mL of distilled water [NOTE 1]. Label bottle "B".

6. To prepare solution C, repeat Steps 1–4, using about 7.5 g of sugar and 42 mL of distilled water [NOTE 1]. Label bottle "C".

7. Solution D is pure water. Pour 50 mL of distilled water into a small bottle. Label bottle "D". This solution is your 0.00% sugar solution.

II. Determining the Densities of Your Sugar Solutions

8. Tare a clean 50-mL beaker.

9. Draw up enough solution D to half fill a clean, dry 10-mL pipet. Use this solution to rinse the inside of the pipet. Allow the rinse solution to drain into a 150-mL beaker, labeled "Discard Solutions".

10. Use the rinsed 10-mL pipet to transfer 10.00 mL of solution D to the tared 50-mL beaker. Measure and record the mass. Pour the contents of the beaker into the drain, diluting with a large amount of running water. Wash the beaker, then rinse with distilled water for reuse.

11. Repeat Steps 8–10 at least two more times. Perform additional determinations, if necessary, until you have obtained three masses that agree within the limits specified by your laboratory instructor.

12. Repeat Steps 8–11, using solutions A, B, and C.

III. Determining the Densities of Commercial Beverage Samples

13. Obtain three commercial beverage samples from your laboratory instructor. Record the identification codes or names of your three samples.

14. Repeat Steps 8–11, using each beverage sample.

15. Pour the contents of your Discard Solutions beaker and any leftover solutions or samples into the drain, diluting with a large amount of running water.

CAUTION ⚠

Wash your hands thoroughly with soap or detergent before leaving the laboratory.

_____   _____   _____
Name   *Section*   *Date*

Data Sheet

I. Preparing Solutions of Known Sugar Content

solution	mass of sugar, g	mass of solution, g
A	_____	_____
B	_____	_____
C	_____	_____
D	0	

II. Determining the Densities of Your Sugar Solutions

	mass of 10.00 mL of solution, g determination			*average mass of 10.00 mL of solution, g*
solution	1	2	3	
A	_____	_____	_____	_____
B	_____	_____	_____	_____
C	_____	_____	_____	_____
D	_____	_____	_____	_____

III. Determining the Densities of Commercial Beverage Samples

identification code or name of beverage	*mass of 10.00 mL of beverage, g determination*			*average mass of 10.00 mL of beverage, g*
	1	2	3	
_____	_____	_____	_____	_____
_____	_____	_____	_____	_____
_____	_____	_____	_____	_____

_____   _____   _____
Name   *Section*   *Date*

Results Sheet

I. Determining the Densities of Your Sugar Solutions

1. Calculate mass percent sugar and average density for solutions *A–D*. Record your results in the following table.

solution	*mass percent sugar, %*	*average density of solution, g/mL*
A	_____	_____
B	_____	_____
C	_____	_____
D	_____	_____

2. On the graph paper supplied, graph your data for solutions *A–D*. Plot average solution density on the *y*-axis and mass percent sugar on the *x*-axis. Do not start your *y*-axis scale at 0. Instead, select *y*-axis scale units so that the lowest value is slightly below the average density of solution *D*, and the highest value is slightly above the average density of solution *C*. Your *x*-axis scale should run from 0 to 20 mass percent sugar. Draw the best straight line defined by your data points.

Alternatively, your laboratory instructor may tell you to use a computer spreadsheet program to graph the data and determine the following equation for the resulting trend line:

$$\text{density, g/mL} = \underbrace{\left(\underline{\hspace{3cm}} \right)}_{\text{slope}} (\text{mass percent sugar, \%}) + \underbrace{\underline{\hspace{3cm}}}_{\text{y-intercept}}$$

II. Determining the Densities of Commercial Beverage Samples

3. Calculate the average density for each of your commercial beverages. Record your results in the following table. Using either your graph or the trend–line equation that you calculated, determine the mass percent sugar for each of your beverages. Record your results in the following table.

identification code or name of beverage	*average density of beverage, g/mL*	*mass percent sugar, %*
_____	_____	_____
_____	_____	_____
_____	_____	_____

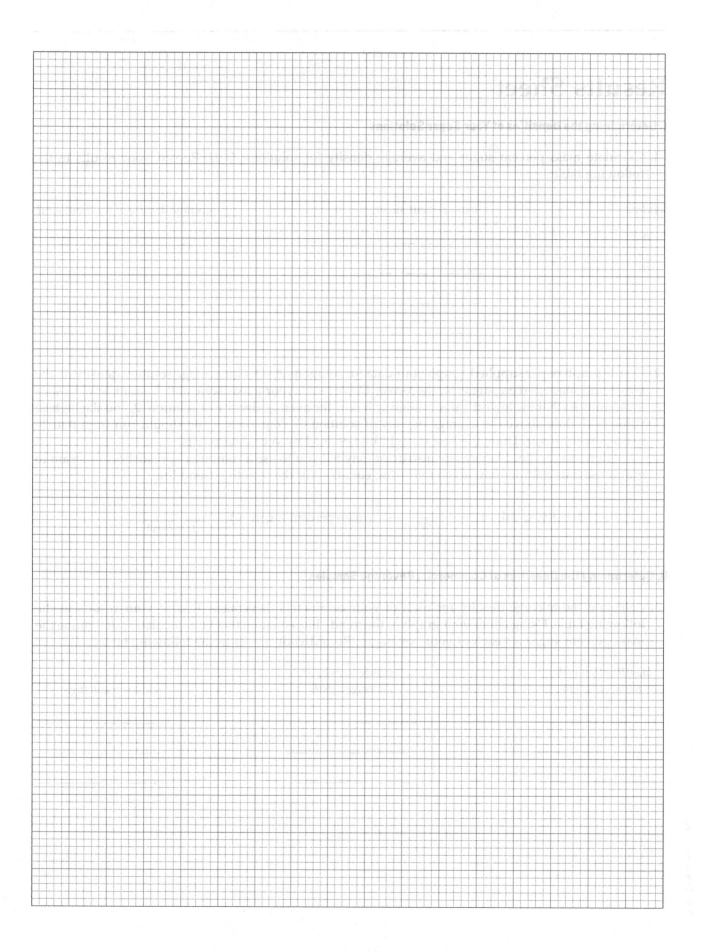

Name   Section   Date

Interpretation of Your Results

Use the spaces provided for the answers and additional paper if necessary.

1. Chemical references list the density of water as 0.998 g/mL at room temperature. Based on this accepted value, calculate the percent error in your average density ($d_{experimental}$) for solution D, using Equation 3:

$$\text{percent error, \%} = \frac{|0.998\,\text{g/mL} - d_{experimental}|}{0.998\,\text{g/mL}}(100\%) \qquad \text{(Eq. 3)}$$

2. (a) Read the can or bottle label for each of your commercial beverage samples, in order to find the Calorie content per serving and the serving size in milliliters.* Calculate Calories per milliliter for each of your beverages.

(b) Prepare a table listing your three beverages, their mass percent sugar, and their Calories/mL. Determine whether or not the sugar content is roughly proportional to the caloric value of the beverages.

(c) Explain any differences (or similarities) in the sugar contents of these beverages.

*This information may be supplied by your laboratory instructor, keyed using sample identification codes.

3. Would cans of each of your beverages float or sink if placed in a tub of water? Briefly explain.

4. In order to use the Procedure in this experiment to analyze freshly squeezed orange juice, you must first filter the pulp from the liquid. Explain why this must be done in order for the Procedure to yield accurate results.

_____   _____   _____

Pre-Laboratory Assignment

1. What precautions should you take when working with the solids and solutions you will use in this experiment?

2. In Step 1 of the Procedure, what is meant by the word, "tare"?

3. (a) A student prepared a solution of ethylene glycol (automotive antifreeze) in distilled water. He mixed about 5 mL of ethylene glycol with about 45 mL of water. The mass of the ethylene glycol was 5.580 g. The total mass of the solution was 49.037 g. Calculate the mass percent ethylene glycol in the solution.

   (b) The student determined the average mass of 10.00 mL of this solution to be 10.063 g. Calculate the average density of the solution.

   (c) In a similar fashion, the student prepared other aqueous solutions of ethylene glycol and measured their densities, obtaining the data shown in the following table. Record your calculated results from (a) and (b) in this table.

mass percent ethylene glycol, %	0.00	_____	22.75	33.22
average density, g/mL	0.993	_____	1.021	1.030

   (d) Using the graph paper supplied, plot average density versus mass percent ethylene glycol. Draw the best straight line through your data points.
   Alternatively, your laboratory instructor may tell you to use a computer spreadsheet program to graph the data and determine the equation of the resulting trend line.

   (e) An aqueous solution of ethylene glycol has a density of 1.010 g/mL. What is the mass percent ethylene glycol in this solution?

4. A student performing this experiment for solutions of sugar in water plotted her data as described in the Procedure. She found that the slope of her trend line was 0.00401 g/mL · % and the y-intercept was 0.995 g/mL. She also found the average density of a lemonade sample to be 1.031 g/mL. Calculate the mass percent sugar in this lemonade sample.

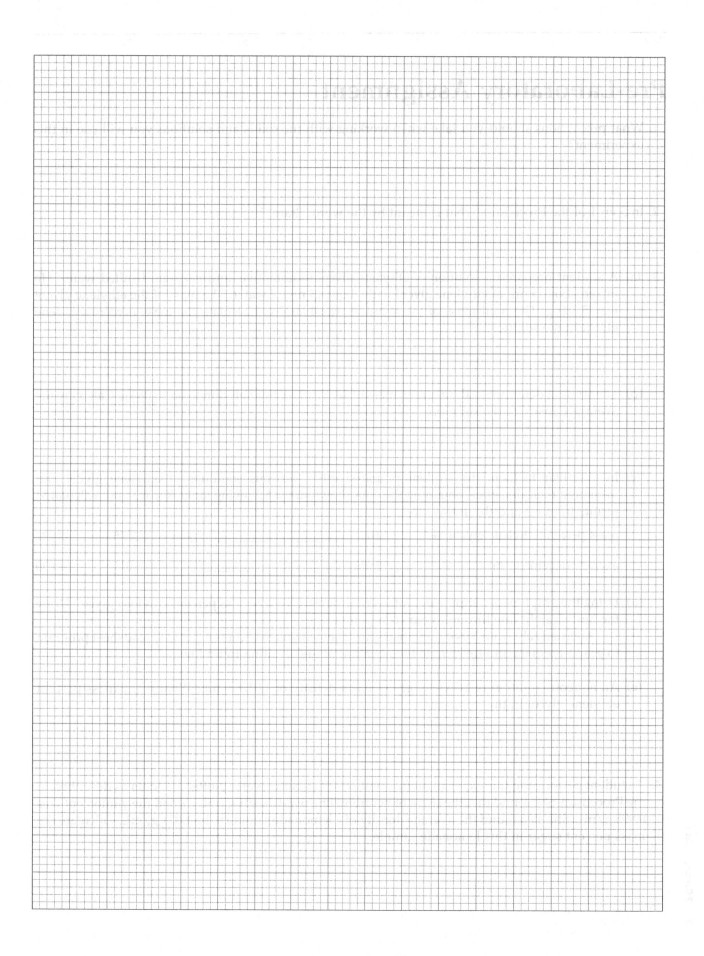

Determining the Water Content of an Ionic Hydrate

*Prepared by Donald F. Clemens, East Carolina University, Warren A. McAllister,
Burroughs Wellcome Co., Greenville, N.C., Marcia L. Gillette, Indiana University
Kokomo, and Henry D. Schreiber, Virginia Military Institute*

PURPOSE OF THE EXPERIMENT

Determine the mass percent of water in an ionic hydrate. Establish the chemical formula of this hydrate.

BACKGROUND REQUIRED

You should be familiar with techniques for measuring mass. You should also be familiar with naming a compound, relating its chemical formula to its composition, and calculating the number of moles of a compound.

BACKGROUND INFORMATION

Ionic Hydrates

Copper(II) sulfate ($CuSO_4$) is a white powder. If we add a few drops of water to this substance, the powder not only absorbs the water, but it also transforms into blue crystals. The reaction is shown in Equation 1.

$$CuSO_4(s) + 5\,H_2O(\ell) \rightarrow CuSO_4 \cdot 5\,H_2O(s) \qquad \text{(Eq. 1)}$$
$$\underset{\text{white}}{} \qquad\qquad\qquad \underset{\text{blue}}{}$$

We call $CuSO_4$ an **anhydrous** compound, which means a compound that does not contain water. We call $CuSO_4 \cdot 5H_2O$ an **ionic hydrate,** which means an ionic solid that contains water molecules within its structure.

$CuSO_4$ is composed of equal numbers of Cu^{2+} and SO_4^{2-} packed in a crystal lattice. The water molecules that combine with an anhydrous compound to form an ionic hydrate are its **waters of hydration**. These water molecules are not just physically trapped within the solid, like water in a sponge, but are chemically bound to specific sites within the hydrate's lattice. Therefore, we include the waters of hydration in the ionic hydrate's chemical formula. The formula for an ionic hydrate consists of the formula for the original anhydrous compound, followed by a raised dot, followed by the number of water molecules. Hence, $CuSO_4 \cdot 5H_2O$ is the formula for the ionic hydrate composed of Cu^{2+}, SO_4^{2-}, and water molecules in a 1:1:5 mole ratio.

To name an ionic hydrate, we begin with the name of the original anhydrous compound. Then we use a prefix to indicate the number of waters of hydration, followed by the word "hydrate". The prefixes are mono-, di-, tri-, tetra-, penta-, hexa-, hepta-, octa-, nona- and deca- for one through ten, respectively. Thus, we identify $CuSO_4 \cdot 5H_2O$ as copper(II) sulfate pentahydrate.

Water Content of Ionic Hydrates

We can decompose an ionic hydrate in order to analyze its water content. For example, careful heating of blue $CuSO_4 \cdot 5H_2O$ yields white anhydrous $CuSO_4$ and water vapor, as shown in Equation 2.

$$CuSO_4 \cdot 5H_2O(s) \xrightarrow{\text{heat}} CuSO_4(s) + 5H_2O(g) \qquad \text{(Eq. 2)}$$
$$\underset{\text{blue}}{} \qquad \underset{\text{white}}{}$$

To determine the water content of an ionic hydrate sample, we measure the mass of the hydrate before and after heating. Based on this analysis, we can express the water content of the hydrate in the following two ways.

First, we can calculate the mass percent of water in the hydrate. The mass of water in a hydrate sample equals the mass lost upon heating. Based on the mass of water and the total sample mass, we can calculate the mass percent of water, using Equation 3.

$$\text{mass percent of water, } \% = \left(\frac{\text{mass of water, g}}{\text{mass of original sample, g}} \right) (100\%) \qquad \text{(Eq. 3)}$$

Second, we can determine the ionic hydrate's chemical formula, which shows how many waters of hydration are present in one unit of hydrate. The mass of the hydrate after heating equals the mass of the anhydrous component. Based on this mass, we can calculate the number of moles of anhydrous compound in the original sample, as well as the number of moles of water given off during heating. If we then divide the number of moles of water by the number of moles of anhydrous compound, as shown in Equation 4, we will obtain the number of waters of hydration in the formula for the hydrate.

$$\text{number of waters of hydration} = \frac{\text{moles of water, mol}}{\text{moles of anhydrous compound, mol}} \qquad \text{(Eq. 4)}$$

Note that the number of waters of hydration is usually an integer. Once we have determined the number of waters of hydration, we can write the chemical formula for the hydrate, beginning with the formula for the anhydrous compound, followed by a raised dot, followed by the number of waters of hydration.

Example

Suppose you obtain a 5.00-g sample of an ionic hydrate of calcium sulfate ($CaSO_4$). After heating the hydrate to drive off the water, you measure the remaining mass as 3.95 g.

Problem 1 Determine the mass percent of water in this ionic hydrate.

Solution We subtract the mass after heating from the initial sample mass to determine the mass of water vapor driven off.

$$\text{mass of water, g} = 5.00\,\text{g} - 3.95\;\text{g} = 1.05\;\text{g}$$

We then calculate the mass percent of water in this ionic hydrate using Equation 3.

$$\text{mass percent of water, \%} = \frac{1.05\;\text{g}}{5.00\;\text{g}}(100\%) = 21.0\%$$

Problem 2 Determine the chemical formula for the hydrate.

Solution Only anhydrous $CaSO_4$ remains after heating. Based on this mass (3.95 g) and the molar mass of $CaSO_4$ (136.14 g/mol), we calculate the number of moles of anhydrous compound in the original sample.

$$\text{moles of anhydrous } CaSO_4, \text{mol} = \frac{3.95\;\text{g}}{136.15\;\text{g/mol}} = 2.90 \times 10^{-2}\;\text{mol}$$

Next, based on the molar mass of water (18.02 g/mol), we calculate the number of moles of water in the original sample.

$$\text{moles of water, mol} = \frac{1.05\;\text{g}}{18.02\;\text{g/mol}} = 5.83 \times 10^{-2}\;\text{mol}$$

Finally, we use Equation 4 to determine the number of waters of hydration in the hydrate's chemical formula.

$$\text{number of waters of hydration} = \frac{5.83 \times 10^{-2}\;\text{mol}}{2.90 \times 10^{-2}\;\text{mol}} = 2.01 \approx 2$$

Therefore, we write the formula for this hydrate as $CaSO_4 \cdot 2H_2O$.

Problem 3 Name this ionic hydrate.

Solution We start with the name of the anhydrous compound, followed with the appropriate prefix for two waters of hydration (di-), followed by "hydrate". The name is calcium sulfate dihydrate.

PROCEDURE

CAUTION

Wear departmentally approved safety goggles while doing this experiment.

Use caution when working with your unknown ionic hydrate, because it could be toxic and an irritant.

Always use crucible tongs when handling the crucible and cover, in order to avoid contaminating the crucible and cover with finger oils, and to prevent burns when the crucible is hot.

NOTE: Record all measurements on your Data Sheet.

Record all masses to either the nearest milligram (0.001 g) or centigram (0.01 g), as indicated by your laboratory instructor.

Heating a crucible and contents to constant mass means repeating the cycle of heating, cooling, and weighing until you obtain two consecutive mass measurements that do not vary significantly. The laboratory instructor will give you the acceptable variation range.

I. Heating the Crucible to Constant Mass

NOTE 1: The laboratory instructor can tell you how to adjust your Bunsen burner in order to control the flame temperature.

1. Wash a crucible using detergent. Rinse, and dry the crucible.

2. Using crucible tongs, place the crucible on a clay triangle, supported by an iron ring attached to a ring stand, as shown in Figure 1.

3. Using a Bunsen burner flame, heat the crucible to thoroughly dry it. [NOTE 1] Heat slowly at first, then more vigorously, until the crucible bottom glows red. Using crucible tongs, remove the crucible from the triangle. Place the crucible on a heat-resistant surface for about 3 min. Then transfer it to a desiccator, and allow it to cool to room temperature (about 5 min).

4. Measure and record the mass of the cooled crucible.

5. Repeat Steps 2–4 until you have heated the crucible to constant mass.

II. Determining the Hydrate's Water Content

6. Obtain a sample of an ionic hydrate from your laboratory instructor. Record its identification code.

7. Transfer at least 1 g of your ionic hydrate into the crucible. Measure and record the exact mass of crucible plus sample.

8. Using crucible tongs, place your crucible and its contents on the clay triangle, as shown in Figure 1. Place a crucible cover on top, slightly ajar,

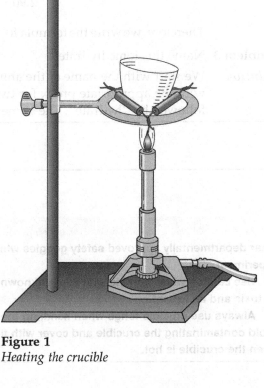

Figure 1
Heating the crucible

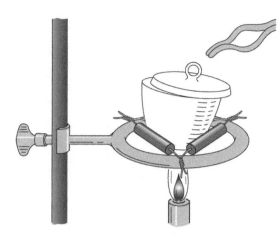

Figure 2
Heating the crucible and sample

© 2002 Cengage Learning

NOTE 2: Do not heat your crucible too vigorously, because that may cause the anhydrous compound to start to decompose.

as shown in Figure 2. [NOTE 2] Heat the crucible and contents for 5 min, using a low Bunsen burner flame. Then heat for 5 min more, using a medium flame. Finally, heat the crucible for an additional 10 min, using a hot flame, but do *not* allow the crucible bottom to turn red.

9. Transfer your covered crucible to a heat-resistant surface. Allow it to cool for about 3 min. Then transfer the covered crucible to a desiccator. Allow the crucible and contents to cool to room temperature (about 5 min).

10. Remove the crucible cover. Measure and record the mass of crucible plus contents.

11. Reheat the crucible, cover, and contents for 10 min, with the cover ajar as before, using a hot flame. Once again, do not allow the crucible bottom to turn red. Then repeat Steps 9 and 10.

12. Repeat Step 11 until you have heated the crucible and contents to constant mass.

13. Transfer your crucible contents into the appropriately labeled collection container.

14. The laboratory instructor may tell you to do a second determination, using another sample of your assigned hydrate.

15. When you have completed all of your determinations, wash and dry your crucible and cover.

CAUTION

Wash your hands thoroughly with soap or detergent before leaving the laboratory.

Name	*Section*	*Date*

Data Sheet

I. Heating the Crucible to Constant Mass

determination

1   2

mass of empty crucible:

after first heating and cooling, g   _____   _____

after second heating and cooling, g   _____   _____

after third heating and cooling, g (as needed)   _____   _____

II. Determining the Hydrate's Water Content

identification code   _____

mass of crucible plus sample, g   _____   _____

mass of crucible and contents:

after first heating and cooling, g   _____   _____

after second heating and cooling, g   _____   _____

after third heating and cooling, g (as needed)   _____   _____

after fourth heating and cooling, g (as needed) _____   _____

Result Sheet

II. Determining the Hydrate's Water Content

identification code _____

When weighing to constant mass, use the mass determined from your last heating and cooling cycle for your calculations. Summarize your calculations in the following table.

	determination	
	1	2
mass of original ionic hydrate sample, g	_____	_____
mass of water given off by sample, g	_____	_____
mass percent of water in ionic hydrate, %	_____	_____
average mass percent of water in ionic hydrate, %	_____	
mass of anhydrous compound, g	_____	_____
chemical formula of anhydrous compound (obtained from the laboratory instructor)	_____	
molar mass of anhydrous compound, g/mol	_____	
number of moles of anhydrous compound, mol	_____	_____
number of moles of water given off by sample, mol	_____	_____
number of moles of water per mole of anhydrous compound = number of waters of hydration in hydrate formula	_____	_____
average number of waters of hydration in hydrate formula	_____	
chemical formula for ionic hydrate	_____	

_____   _____   _____
Name   *Section*   *Date*

Interpretation of Your Results

Use the spaces provided for the answers and additional paper if necessary.

1. Name your ionic hydrate.

2. Write a balanced chemical equation showing what happened when you heated your ionic hydrate in the crucible.

3. How many grams of water are present in 5.00 g of your ionic hydrate?

4. A desiccant is an anhydrous compound that absorbs water vapor from the atmosphere. The more water it can absorb per gram, the better a desiccant it is. Explain which of the following compounds would make the best desiccant: your anhydrous compound, $CaSO_4$, or $CuSO_4$.

5. Was it important to heat your product to constant mass? If you had not done so, how would it have affected your results?

_____   _____   _____

Pre-Laboratory Assignment

1. Why is it necessary to always use crucible tongs when handling your crucible in this experiment?

2. Define each of the following terms as they relate to this experiment:

(a) anhydrous compound

(b) ionic hydrate

3. Briefly differentiate an ionic hydrate from a compound that is simply wet.

4. Suppose you used the Procedure in this experiment to decompose 1.047 g of an ionic hydrate. You recovered 0.950 g of strontium oxalate (SrC_2O_4) after heating the sample to constant mass.

(a) Determine the mass of water given off during heating.

(b) Calculate the mass percent of water in the ionic hydrate.

(c) Calculate the number of moles of anhydrous compound in the sample.

(d) Calculate the number of moles of water given off during heating.

(e) Calculate the number of waters of hydration in the chemical formula for this ionic hydrate.

(f) Write the chemical formula and name for this ionic hydrate.

Determining the Empirical Formula of a Compound Containing Copper and Chlorine

Prepared by M. L. Gillette, Indiana University Kokomo, and
Don Stafford, East Central University, OK

PURPOSE OF THE EXPERIMENT

Determine the empirical formula of a compound containing copper and chlorine.

BACKGROUND REQUIRED

You should be familiar with basic laboratory techniques for measuring mass. You should understand the concepts associated with stoichiometry.

BACKGROUND INFORMATION

A **compound** is a substance composed of two or more elements. The **empirical formula** of a compound is an expression of the simplest whole-number molar ratio of the elements making up that compound. For example, water (H_2O) and hydrogen peroxide (H_2O_2) are both compounds composed of hydrogen (H) and oxygen (O). However, the empirical formula of water is H_2O, while that of hydrogen peroxide is HO.

According to the **law of constant composition**, the molar ratio of elements in a specific compound is a constant, regardless of the compound's source or method of preparation. Once we determine the individual masses of each element composing a specific compound, we can determine the empirical formula of that compound.

Example

Problem The mass of a clean, dry crucible was 10.443 g. The mass of the crucible after the addition of a sample of shiny brown copper (Cu) wire was 11.229 g. The wire was then covered with yellow powdered elemental sulfur (S_8). The crucible was heated until all the

Cu reacted with S_8, and the excess S_8 was burned off. After cooling, the crucible plus black reaction product weighed 11.432 g. Determine the empirical formula of the reaction product, Cu_xS_y.

Solution **(1)** *Calculate the mass of Cu reacted.*

$$11.229 \text{ g} - 10.443 \text{ g} = 0.786 \text{ g}$$

(2) *Calculate the mass of Cu_xS_y formed.*

$$11.432 \text{ g} - 10.443 \text{ g} = 0.989 \text{ g}$$

(3) *Calculate the mass of sulfur (S) in the Cu_xS_y formed, using Equation 1.*

$$\text{mass of S, g} = (\text{mass of } Cu_xS_y, \text{g}) - (\text{mass of Cu, g}) \qquad \text{(Eq. 1)}$$
$$= 0.989 \text{ g} - 0.786 \text{ g} = 0.203 \text{ g}$$

(4) *Calculate the number of moles of Cu present in the Cu_xS_y formed, using Equation 2.*

$$\text{number of moles of Cu present, mol} = (\text{mass of Cu, g})\left(\frac{1 \text{ mol Cu}}{63.55 \text{ g Cu}}\right) \qquad \text{(Eq. 2)}$$
$$= (0.786 \text{ g Cu})\left(\frac{1 \text{ mol Cu}}{63.55 \text{ g Cu}}\right)$$
$$= 1.24 \times 10^{-2} \text{ mol Cu}$$

(5) *Calculate the number of moles of S present in the Cu_xS_y formed, using a modification of Equation 2.*

$$\text{number of moles of S present, mol} = (0.203 \text{ g S})\left(\frac{1 \text{ mol S}}{32.06 \text{ g S}}\right) = 6.33 \times 10^{-3} \text{ mol S}$$

(6) *Determine the molar ratio of Cu to S in Cu_xS_y. To do so, divide the number of moles of each element by the smaller of the two numbers of moles. Round each quotient, if close to a whole number, to the nearest whole number. Use the results to write the empirical formula of the reaction product.*

$$\frac{1.24 \times 10^{-2} \text{ mol Cu}}{6.33 \times 10^{-3}} = 1.96 \approx 2 \text{ mol Cu}$$

$$\frac{6.33 \times 10^{-3} \text{ mol S}}{6.33 \times 10^{-3}} = 1.00 \text{ mol S}$$

Therefore, the empirical formula of the reaction product is Cu_2S.

In This Experiment

You will determine the empirical formula of copper chloride, by reacting a measured volume of aqueous copper chloride solution with zinc (Zn), then weighing the solid elemental Cu produced.

PROCEDURE

CAUTION

Wear departmentally approved safety goggles while doing this experiment. Always use caution in the laboratory. Many chemicals are potentially harmful. Prevent contact with your eyes, skin, and clothing. Avoid ingesting any of the reagents. Use care when handling hot objects.

NOTE:

- Record all masses to either the nearest milligram (0.001 g) or nearest centigram (0.01 g), as specified by your laboratory instructor.

- Record all data on your Data and Observations sheet.

- Adjust all hot plate settings according to your laboratory instructor's directions.

- If your instructor tells you to perform two determinations simultaneously, follow the Procedure as written with both samples, but label your two evaporating dishes "determination 1" and "determination 2", so you will not mix them up during the heating and weighing processes.

- Dispose of all solids, solutions, and rinses as directed by your laboratory instructor.

- Be careful not to spill any solids during the transfer steps in the procedure. Such losses will affect your calculated results.

CAUTION

Copper chloride solution is toxic and an irritant.

1. Obtain 25.0 mL of copper chloride solution in a 50-mL graduated cylinder. Transfer this solution into a clean 150-mL beaker. Record the mass of copper chloride in 25.0 mL of the solution, using the data on the reagent bottle label.

   Rinse the graduated cylinder with 5 mL of distilled or deionized water. Transfer the rinse into the 150-mL beaker.

2. Obtain a clean, precut strip of Zn and determine and record its mass.

NOTE: In Step 3, avoid letting the tips of the crucible tongs contact the solution. The tongs may react with the solution.

3. Tilt the 150-mL beaker slightly. Using crucible tongs, transfer the weighed Zn into the copper chloride solution. Allow the Zn to gently slide down the inner beaker wall, in order to avoid any solution loss due to splashing.

CAUTION

Hydrochloric acid (HCl) is toxic and corrosive.

4. Stir the reaction mixture with a clean, glass stirring rod, so that the solid Cu product will not adhere to the Zn. Continue stirring until the blue color has disappeared. Then add 5–10 drops of 10% HCl to the solution. Thoroughly stir.

5. Remove all unreacted Zn from the solution, using crucible tongs. Scrape any Cu adhering to the Zn back into the beaker, using a metal spatula. Dry the Zn with paper towels.

   Determine and record the mass of the dried Zn. Discard the Zn as directed.

6. Carefully decant the colorless solution from the 150-mL beaker into a second 150-mL beaker. Discard the solution as directed. Rinse the second beaker with tap water. Discard the rinses as directed.

7. Rinse the solid Cu as follows, in order to remove any zinc chloride adhering to it. Begin by pouring 10 mL of distilled water into the 150-mL beaker containing the Cu. Stir the mixture thoroughly with a stirring rod. Decant the liquid into the empty 150-mL beaker. Rinse the Cu a second time by repeating this process. Discard rinses as directed.

NOTE: Always handle your evaporating dish using crucible tongs, in order to avoid contaminating the dish with finger oils and to prevent burns from a hot dish.

In order to accurately determine the mass of an object, the object must be at room temperature.

---

8. Using crucible tongs, place a clean, dry evaporating dish on a hot plate. Heat the dish for approximately 10 min.

   Transfer the hot dish from the hot plate to a ceramic-centered wire gauze on your laboratory bench. As soon as you can feel no heat when you hold your hand 1–2 cm from the dish, use tongs to transfer the dish to a balance. Determine and record the mass of the dish.

NOTE: Your laboratory instructor will give you specific directions for drying the Cu in Step 10. Avoid overheating the evaporating dish and its contents. Overheating will cause the hot Cu to react with atmospheric oxygen (O_2), forming black copper oxide.

---

9. Use distilled water from a wash bottle to rinse all visible traces of Cu from your beaker into your weighed evaporating dish.

   Decant as much of the water as possible from the evaporating dish. Carefully tip the dish slightly to collect any remaining water near the edge of the dish. Remove some of this water by dipping the corner of a clean paper towel into it. Repeat this process until you have removed as much residual water as possible.

10. Dry the Cu by placing the evaporating dish and its contents on a hot plate. Heat the dish and its contents over low to moderate heat to evaporate the liquid. When the Cu appears to be almost dry, stir it with a clean, glass stirring rod while continuing to heat.

   When the Cu appears completely dry, transfer the evaporating dish from the hot plate to a ceramic-centered wire gauze on your laboratory bench. Allow the dish to cool to room temperature. Then determine the mass of the dish plus contents. Record this mass as "first heating".

11. Transfer the dish and its contents back to the hot plate. Reheat for 2–5 min. Then, remove the dish from the hot plate. Allow the dish to cool to room temperature again. Then, determine the mass of the dish plus contents. Record this mass as "second heating".

If your two mass determinations are not within 0.01 g of each other, consult your laboratory instructor for further directions. If the mass of your dish plus Cu *increases* between the first and second heatings, also consult your laboratory instructor.

Once you obtain two satisfactory mass determinations, have your laboratory instructor initial your Data and Observations sheet. Discard the Cu residue as directed by your laboratory instructor.

CAUTION ⚠

Wash your hands thoroughly with soap or detergent before leaving the laboratory.

Name	*Partner*	*Section*	*Date*

Post-Laboratory Questions

Use the spaces provided for the answers and additional paper if necessary.

1. If you performed two determinations, use your experimental results to answer the following questions. If you performed only one determination, answer the questions using the results you would expect to obtain if you performed a second determination.

    (a) Is your calculated empirical formula of Cu_xCl_y the same for both determinations?

    (b) Should the calculated empirical formula for Cu_xCl_y be the same for both determinations? Briefly explain.

2. What effect would each of the following experimental errors have on the calculated number of moles of Cu in copper chloride in this experiment? Indicate if the calculated number of moles of Cu would be too low, too high, or unchanged and briefly explain.

    (a) A student removed the Zn from the reaction mixture while the solution was still blue.

    (b) A few tiny pieces of Zn were left adhering to the Cu when a student dried and weighed the Cu.

    (c) At the start of the experiment, a student actually added 7.5 g of Zn, but he mistakenly recorded 5.5 g as the amount added.

3. (a) Write your experimentally determined empirical formula for Cu_xCl_y into the chemical equation below, which describes the reaction you performed in the laboratory. Then balance the equation.

    _____ (aq, blue) + Zn(s, silvery) → Cu(s, brown) + $ZnCl_2$(aq, colorless)

(b) Based on the data from each of your determinations, calculate the mass of Zn consumed by the reaction described by the chemical equation in (a).

determination 1 _____   determination 2 _____

(c) Calculate the number of moles of Zn consumed for each determination.

determination 1 _____   determination 2 _____

(d) Compare the molar ratio of Cu to Zn in your balanced chemical equation in (a) with the molar ratio determined using your experimental results. Briefly account for any differences between these ratios.

4. A laboratory analysis of an unknown compound showed that it consisted of 60.00% C, 4.48% H, and 35.53% O by mass. Calculate the empirical formula of the unknown compound.

_____   _____   _____   _____
Name   *Partner*   *Section*   *Date*

Data and Observations

mass of copper chloride in 25.0 mL of solution, g _____

	determination	
	1	*2*
mass of Zn strip, g	_____	_____
mass of empty evaporating dish, g	_____	_____
mass of dried, unreacted Zn, g	_____	_____
mass of evaporating dish plus Cu, g		
first heating	_____	_____
second heating	_____	_____
third heating (if necessary)	_____	_____
fourth heating (if necessary)	_____	_____
laboratory instructor's initials	_____	_____

_____   _____   _____   _____
Name   *Partner*   *Section*   *Date*

Calculations and Conclusions

Show your calculations for at least one determination in the spaces provided. Remember to include units with all calculated results.

1. Calculate the mass of Cu produced.

determination 1 _____   determination 2 _____

2. Calculate the mass of chlorine (Cl) in your original Cu_xCl_y sample, using a modification of Equation 1 (substitute Cu_xCl_y for Cu_xS_y).

determination 1 _____   determination 2 _____

3. Calculate the number of moles of Cu present in your Cu_xCl_y sample, using Equation 2.

determination 1 _____   determination 2 _____

4. Calculate the number of moles of Cl present in your Cu_xCl_y sample, using a modification of Equation 2.

determination 1 _____   determination 2 _____

5. Determine the molar ratio of Cu to Cl in Cu_xCl_y, by dividing each number of moles present by the smaller of the two numbers of moles. Use these ratios to write the empirical formula of copper chloride.

determination 1 _____   determination 2 _____

Name	*Partner*	*Section*	*Date*

Pre-Laboratory Assignment

1. List two reasons for using crucible tongs to handle the evaporating dish in this experiment.

2. (a) Acetylene (C_2H_2) is a hydrocarbon that is commonly burned in welders' torches. What is the empirical formula of acetylene?

(b) Ethylene glycol ($C_2H_6O_2$) is commonly used as antifreeze in automobile radiators. What is the empirical formula of ethylene glycol?

3. (a) Why is it important to allow your evaporating dish and its contents to cool to room temperature, before weighing them?

(b) How will you determine when your evaporating dish and its contents have cooled to room temperature?

(c) Why is it important not to overheat your Cu while you are drying it in the evaporating dish?

4. A student followed the Procedure of this experiment to determine the empirical formula of a compound of iron (Fe) and Cl. To do so, she added a 2.15-g piece of Zn to a solution containing 1.750 g of Fe_xCl_y. After the reaction was complete, she isolated 0.771 g of Fe.

(a) Calculate the mass of Cl in the Fe_xCl_y solution.

(b) Calculate the number of moles of Fe present in the Fe_xCl_y solution.

(c) Calculate the number of moles of Cl present in the Fe_xCl_y solution.

(d) Determine the molar ratio of Fe to Cl in the compound. Use this ratio to write the empirical formula of the compound of iron and chlorine.

Name _____ Date _____

Pre-Laboratory Assignment

1. List two reasons for using crucible tongs to handle the evaporating dish in this experiment.

2. (a) Acetylene (C_2H_2) is a hydrocarbon that is commonly burned in welder's torches. What is the empirical formula of acetylene?

(b) Ethylene glycol ($C_2H_6O_2$) is commonly used as antifreeze in automobile radiators. What is the empirical formula of ethylene glycol?

3. (a) Why is it important to allow your watch/vapor... dish and its contents to cool to room temperature before weighing them?

(b) How will you determine when your evaporating dish and its contents have cooled to room temperature?

(c) Why is it important not to overheat your compound while you are drying it in the evaporating dish?

4. A student followed the Procedure of this experiment to determine the empirical formula of a compound of iron (Fe) and Cl. In the experiment, she added a 2.13-g piece of Zn to a solution containing 1.784 g of $FeCl_3$. After the reaction was complete, she isolated 0.771 g of Fe.

(a) Calculate the mass of Cl in the $FeCl_3$ solution.

(b) Calculate the number of moles of Fe present in the $FeCl_3$ solution.

(c) Calculate the number of moles of Cl present in the $FeCl_3$ solution.

(d) Determine the molar ratio of Fe to Cl in the compound. Use this ratio to write the empirical formula of the compound of iron and chlorine.

Synthesis of a Compound (Alum)
from Scrap Aluminum

OBJECTIVE To prepare common alum, $KAl(SO_4)_2 \cdot 12H_2O$, from a discarded aluminum beverage can or from a piece of aluminum foil.

CONCEPT TO BE TESTED Useful compounds may be synthesized directly from scrap materials.

TEXT REFERENCES (1) Whitten, Davis, Peck, Stanley: 3.4 - 3.5, 22.6 (2) Kotz, Treichel: p 86, 21.5 (3) Masterton, Hurley: 20.1 (4) Moore, Stanitski, Jurs: 11.4

LABORATORY MANUAL REFERENCES (1) Do not perform this experiment until you clearly understand how to handle any chemical or procedural hazards in a safe manner so that you prevent injury to yourself or others. Study Chemical Safety and Rules, pp 29-31 (2) The material covered in Background III: Chemical Reactions in Aqueous Solution and Syntheses are basic to the understanding of this experiment. (3) Laboratory Techniques Sect. A - Handling Chemicals, Sect. B - Determination of Mass and Weight, Sect. E - Heating and Evaporating Liquids, Sect. F.2 - Seperation Techniques. (4) App. B - Formulas, Names and Charges of Some Common Ions, App. G - Molecular and Ionic Chemical Equations are basic to the understanding of this experiment.

INTRODUCTION

Aluminum is the most abundant metal in the earth's surface (7.5% by mass). The abundance of aluminum, coupled with its attractive combination of physical and chemical properties, accounts for the fact that it is one of the principal raw materials used in manufacturing processes. Production of aluminum from raw materials is an energy intensive process.

"Alum" is a generic term that describes hydrated double salts of certain metals having the generalized formula, $(MM'(SO_4)_2 \cdot 12H_2O)$, in which M (univalent) is commonly Na^+, K^+, NH_4^+, or Rb^+ and M' (trivalent) is commonly Al^{3+}, Ga^{3+}, V^{3+}, Cr^{3+}, Mn^{3+}, Fe^{3+}, or Co^{3+}. True alums crystallize in well-defined octahedral shapes and many are beautifully colored, particularly those containing d-transition metals. The ancient Egyptians, Greeks, and Romans used alum as a mordant in dyeing cloth. A mordant contains metal ions that bind dyes to the fabric. Presently alum is used to harden photographic film, to prepare pickles, as a mordant, and for other purposes.

Although the mass of a single aluminum can is quite small, the large number of such containers produced each year means that a very large tonnage of the metal is utilized. Since the metal is not consumed rapidly by corrosion, the amount of scrap aluminum grows rapidly while the available supply of raw materials for the manufacture of aluminum decreases. Environmental problems thus created are typical of those of several different metals. One obvious solution to the problem is to recycle the used fabricated aluminum into other useful metallic objects or into aluminum compounds. Aluminum metal can be recovered from scrap by melting the metal and separating it from solids and volatile impurities. This process uses a large amount of energy. Chemical recovery methods which do not use a lot of energy and use cheap chemicals are highly desirable.

Although this experiment illustrates a chemical recovery process in which waste aluminum is converted chemically into an an industrially important aluminum compound, hydrated potassium aluminum sulfate, $KAl(SO_4)_2 \cdot 12H_2O$, or common alum, the method of preparation in this experiment is not the way alum is obtained for use in industry nor is this a method commonly used to recycle scrap aluminum. Both of these processes are far too complex for general chemistry labs. Nevertheless, this experiment will illustrate an interesting example of turning environmental waste into a useful compound.

The following paragraph describes the reactions you will use to synthesize alum. Metallic aluminum dissolves in aqueous solutions of strong bases such as potassium hydroxide to form hydrogen and a soluble salt containing the complex ion, $Al(OH)_4^-$ (Eq.s 1 & 1a). (NOTE: "a" equations are total ionic equations.)

$$2Al(s) + 2KOH(aq) + 6H_2O(\ell) \longrightarrow 2KAl(OH)_4(aq) + 3H_2(g) \qquad \text{(Eq. 1)}$$

$$2Al(s) + 2[K^+(aq) + OH^-(aq)] + 6H_2O(\ell) \longrightarrow 2[K^+(aq) + Al(OH)_4^-(aq)] + 3H_2(g) \qquad \text{(Eq. 1a)}$$

Aluminum oxide and aluminum hydroxide are amphoteric, i.e., they react with and dissolve in solutions of strong acids as well as soluble bases. After the aluminum has dissolved, the excess potassium hydroxide is neutralized by the addition of a limited amount of sulfuric acid. Sulfuric acid also converts the complex ion, $Al(OH)_4^-$, to insoluble aluminum hydroxide, $Al(OH)_3$ (Eqs. 2 & 2a).

$$2KAl(OH)_4(aq) + H_2SO_4(aq) \longrightarrow 2Al(OH)_3(s) + K_2SO_4(aq) + 2H_2O(\ell) \qquad \text{(Eq. 2)}$$

$$2[K^+(aq) + Al(OH)_4^-(aq)] + [2H^+(aq) + SO_4^{2-}(aq)] \longrightarrow$$
$$2Al(OH)_3(s) + [2K^+(aq) + SO_4^{2-}(aq)] + 2H_2O(\ell) \qquad \text{(Eq. 2a)}$$

The insoluble aluminum hydroxide is neutralized by excess sulfuric acid to form aluminum sulfate, $Al_2(SO_4)_3$, a water soluble ionic compound (Eqs. 3 &3a).

$$2Al(OH)_3(s) + 3H_2SO_4(aq) \longrightarrow Al_2(SO_4)_3(aq) + 6H_2O(\ell) \qquad \text{(Eq. 3)}$$

$$2Al(OH)_3(s) + 3[2H^+(aq) + SO_4^{2-}(aq)] \longrightarrow [2Al^{3+}(aq) + 3SO_4^{2-}(aq)] + 6H_2O(\ell) \qquad \text{(Eq. 3a)}$$

As the solution is cooled, the double salt, $KAl(SO_4)_2 \bullet 12H_2O$, hydrated potassium aluminum sulfate, crystallizes out of the solution (Eq.4). It is collected by filtration.

$$K^+(aq) + Al^{3+}(aq) + 2SO_4^{2-}(aq) + 12H_2O(\ell) \longrightarrow KAl(SO_4)_2 \bullet 12H_2O(s) \qquad \text{(Eq. 4)}$$

CAUTION! YOU MUST WEAR DEPARTMENTALLY APPROVED EYE PROTECTION AT ALL TIMES YOU ARE IN THE LABORATORY!! KEEP ALL REACTION VESSELS WELL AWAY FROM YOUR FACE!!

PROCEDURE

NOTE: Many beverage cans are not aluminum, but are alloys that dissolve slowly. If you have an aluminum can, use a 1 inch by 2 inch piece for this experiment. Sandpaper it to remove as much paint and lacquer as possible before you begin. You instructor may choose to provide a piece of aluminum foil as a source of "scrap" aluminum.

Step 1.   Obtain a piece of aluminum (approximately 0.5-0.9 gram) from your lab instructor. Weigh the piece of **aluminum** to the nearest 0.001 gram. Record the mass on the REPORT FORM (1). Place the aluminum in the bottom of a clean 250 mL beaker.

CAUTION! KOH SOLUTION IS VERY CORROSIVE AND WILL DISSOLVE CLOTHING AND DAMAGE SKIN. WASH YOUR SKIN IMMEDIATELY WITH LOTS OF WATER IF YOU COME IN CONTACT WITH KOH.

Step 2.   Add **35 mL of 2 *M* KOH, potassium hydroxide,** to the beaker.

CAUTION! KEEP FLAMES FROM THE TOP OF THE BEAKER IN WHICH HYDROGEN IS BEING PRODUCED. PERFORM THIS STEP IN A HOOD BEHIND THE SAFETY SHIELD BECAUSE LARGE AMOUNTS OF HYDRO-GEN GAS WILL BE EVOLVED. H_2 GAS BURNS EXPLOSIVELY IN O_2 (AIR).

Step 3.   If the reaction proceeds very slowly, place the beaker on a wire gauze on a ring stand and heat the solution VERY GENTLY AND WITH CAUTION over a small flame. (NOTE: The reaction is very exothermic and will provide its own heat.)

Step 4.   When the reaction is complete (no more bubbles of gas are formed), remove the heat from the beaker and allow the solution to cool to room temperature. If the solution contains no solid residue, go to step 7 (otherwise continue to Step 5).

Step 5.   Prepare a filter by wedging a small plug of **glass wool** into the bottom of a funnel. Place a 150 mL or 250 mL clean beaker below the funnel stem, then pour the solution through the glass wool filter slowly.

Step 6.   Use a wash bottle to rinse all the solution out of the beaker in which the aluminum was dissolved. Direct the stream of water around the top of the beaker to wash down the sides also. *Do not use more than 20 mL of water.* (NOTE: It is better to use four 5 mL rinses in sequence rather than 20 mL all at once.) Pour the wash water through the glass wool filter so that it is added to the solution that contains the dissolved aluminum.

Step 7.   Add ten drops of **methyl red** indicator to the clear solution and cool the solution and beaker in an ice bath for 5 minutes. (NOTE: Methyl red is yellow in basic solutions and red in acidic solutions.)

CAUTION! HANDLE H_2SO_4 SOLUTIONS WITH CARE SINCE THEY ARE VERY CORROSIVE. WASH YOUR SKIN WITH LOTS OF WATER IF YOU COME IN CONTACT WITH H_2SO_4. USE BAKING SODA TO NEUTRALIZE ANY SPILLED ACID.

Step 8.   Obtain **8 mL of 6 M H_2SO_4** in a 150 mL beaker and cool in an ice bath.

Step 9.   Add the **6 M H_2SO_4** *to the cold solution from Step 7* a *few milliliters at a time with vigorous stirring* until the solution just turns *red*. Avoid adding excess H_2SO_4. (NOTE: The addition of H_2SO_4 will cause $Al(OH)_3$ to precipitate as white lumps, but additional H_2SO_4 will dissolve $Al(OH)_3$ to give a clear solution. Dissolve the precipitate as quickly as you can because it will change to a hydrated oxide which dissolves very slowly.)

Step 10.   Heat the solution GENTLY only after most of the precipitate has dissolved and stir vigorously until all the $Al(OH)_3$ has dissolved. The hot solution should be (red) and contain no suspended solids. If it is not red, carefully add a **few drops of 6 M H_2SO_4** until it is red.

Step 11.   Cool the clear, red solution in an ice bath for 20-30 minutes with occasional stirring. Well-defined crystals of alum should form.

Step 12.   While the solution is cooling, prepare a Buchner funnel for vacuum filtration (Figure 1). Select a piece of filter paper that fits into the funnel properly, and wet the paper to seat it. Attach the filter flask to the aspirator. Gently turn on the water for the aspirator . The moist paper should be flat and wrinkle-free in the bottom of the funnel. Ask your instructor to check your apparatus before you begin the filtration.

Step 13. Turn the water on full force so that the aspirator produces the best vacuum for filtration. (NOTE: Put a large beaker under the aspirator outlet to prevent splashing water.)

Step 14. Transfer the alum crystals onto the filter paper with your stirring rod and let the aspirator pull air through them. (NOTE: If 45 minutes or more is left in the laboratory period, perform Step 15. If less time is available, go to Step 16.)

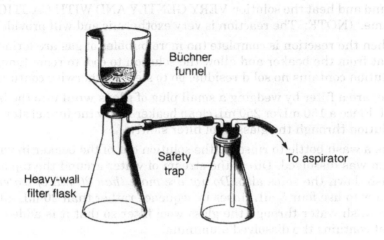

Figure 1 Vacuum filtration apparatus

Step 15. Pour the filtrate solution from the filter flask back into the same beaker and evaporate it to approximately 1/2 its original volume. Cool the solution in an ice bath 20-30 minutes and then filter the second crop of crystals through the same filter with the first crystals.

CAUTION! KEEP OPEN FLAMES AWAY FROM THE FLAMMABLE ETHYL ALCOHOL.

Step 16. Wash the crystals once by drizzling **20 mL of ethyl alcohol** over them. Allow the vacuum to continue for 3-5 minutes. Dry the crystals and filter paper under a heat lamp or in an oven for several minutes. (NOTE: Alum melts at 92°C.)

Step 17. Weigh a small, dry, clean beaker (100-150 mL) to the nearest 0.001 gram. Record this value on the REPORT FORM(17).

Step 18. Transfer the dry crystals to the weighed beaker. Weigh the beaker and crystals to the nearest 0.001 gram. Calculate the mass of the alum that you recovered. Record this value on the REPORT FORM (18). Show your crystals to your instructor and have your report form initialed.

Step 19. Make calculations for the moles of aluminum used (19a), for the theoretical yield of moles of alum (19b), for the theoretical yield of grams of alum (19c) and the percent yield of alum (19d), and record these values on your REPORT FORM(19).

Name _____   Lab Instructor _____

Date _____   Lab Section _____

Prelab questions

1. a. List the chemical hazards in this experiment.

    b. Describe the procedures used in this experiment that hazardous.

    c. Describe the procedures you will follow to make handling of these hazardous chemicals safe for you and for others in your lab.

2. Give a requirement for the manufacture of aluminum from its natually occuring compounds, bauxite ($Al_2O_3 \cdot 2H_2O$), etc., that makes the production of aluminum an expensive process. (Refer to your text.)

3. List a method of recycling waste aluminum.

4.   What are some uses of alums?

5.   How many mL of 2.0 M KOH would be required to react with (dissolve) 2.38 g of pure aluminum (Appendix H discusses molarity, M)?

6.   a.   How many grams of $KAl(SO_4)_2 \bullet 12H_2O$ could be produced from 1.83 g of aluminum?

      b.   If you recovered 6.20 g of alum from this preparation, calculate the percent yield.

REPORT FORM:

Name _____

The Preparation of Common Alum
from Scrap Aluminum

Lab Instructor _____

Lab Section _____

Date _____

Step No.

1. Mass of scrap aluminum used   _____ g

17. Mass of beaker   _____ g

18. Mass of beaker and alum   _____ g

    Mass of alum   _____ g

Instructors approval of crystals   _____ (Initials)

Show your calculations in detail

19a. Number of moles of aluminum used.

_____ mol Al

b. Theoretical yield of alum [$KAl(SO_4)_2 \cdot 12H_2O$] in moles

_____ mol alum

c. Theoretical yield of alum in grams

_____ g alum

d. $$\% \text{ yield of alum} = \frac{\text{actual yield alum}}{\text{theoretical yield alum}} \times 100\%$$

_____ % yield alum

Post-Lab Questions

1. Why should the amount of water used to rinse the beaker in Step 6 be limited to a small volume?

2. Why should a limited amount of H_2SO_4 be used in Steps 9-10?

3.. Write the molecular equations for the following reactions:
    a. For the reaction of aluminum with the KOH.

    b. For the reaction of H_2SO_4 with $Al(OH)_3$.

4. Why should you not dry the alum by heating the alum on a watch glass with a hot flame in Step 16?

Studying Chemical Reactions and Writing Chemical Equations

Prepared by M. L. Gillette, Indiana University Kokomo, and
H. A. Neidig, Lebanon Valley College

PURPOSE OF THE EXPERIMENT

Describe chemical reactions by writing chemical equations based on laboratory observations and information about reactions of different substances.

BACKGROUND INFORMATION

The human digestive process depends on a high concentration of hydrochloric acid (HCl) in the stomach. Sometimes the HCl concentration becomes too high, which causes discomfort ("acid stomach"). When this condition occurs, many people take antacids to help neutralize the excess acid. The active ingredient in many antacids is magnesium hydroxide, $Mg(OH)_2$. When solid $Mg(OH)_2$ mixes with HCl solution, a chemical reaction occurs. We can describe this reaction as: $Mg(OH)_2$ reacts with HCl to produce magnesium chloride ($MgCl_2$) and water (H_2O).

We can make the same statement more concisely by writing a chemical equation for the reaction. A **chemical equation**, the symbolic description of a chemical process, shows the substances that react, the **reactants**, and the substances that form as a result of a chemical change, the **products**. An arrow indicates that the process occurs and is read "yields." The chemical equation for the reaction of $Mg(OH)_2$ and HCl is shown in Equation 1.

$$Mg(OH)_2(s) + 2\,HCl(aq) \rightarrow MgCl_2(aq) + 2\,H_2O(l) \qquad \text{(Eq. 1)}$$

The abbreviations in parentheses following each of the chemical formulas indicate the physical state of each reactant and product. The meanings of the four abbreviations commonly used in equations are summarized in Table 1.

The 2 that appears in front of HCl and H_2O is called a **coefficient**; it indicates that two HCl molecules are consumed and two H_2O molecules are formed in the reaction. Coefficients are used to **balance** an equation so that the reaction involves only a rearrangement of the reactant atoms to form

Table 1 *The meanings of physical-state abbreviations used in chemical equations*

abbreviation	meaning
aq	substance is dissolved in water
g	substance is a gas at reaction temperature and pressure
l	substance is a pure liquid at reaction temperature and pressure
s	substance is a solid that is insoluble in the reaction mixture

products. When no coefficient is shown, as is the case with $Mg(OH)_2$ and $MgCl_2$ in Equation 1, a coefficient of 1 is understood.

The reaction of iron (Fe) with oxygen (O_2) to form iron(III) oxide (Fe_2O_3, ferric oxide) is another familiar reaction. The common name for Fe_2O_3 is rust. The chemical equation for this reaction is given in Equation 2.

$$4\,Fe(s) + 3\,O_2(g) \rightarrow 2\,Fe_2O_3(s) \qquad \text{(Eq. 2)}$$

Notice an important difference between Equations 1 and 2. In the first reaction, *two* reactants produce *two* products whereas in the second reaction, *two* reactants produce only *one* product.

Classifying Chemical Reactions

Many chemical reactions are conveniently classified as one of four major types. This classification is based on the type of chemical transformation that occurs.

Type I: Combination, Synthesis, or Formation Reactions

As the name suggests, a **combination**, or **synthesis reaction**, occurs when two substances combine to form a compound. The reaction in Equation 2 is a combination reaction. Equation 3 is a generalized combination reaction, while Equations 4–6 are specific examples.

$$A + B \rightarrow AB \qquad \text{(Eq. 3)}$$

$$8\,Mg(s) + S_8(s) \rightarrow 8\,MgS(s) \qquad \text{(Eq. 4)}$$

$$2\,Ca(s) + O_2(g) \rightarrow 2\,CaO(s) \qquad \text{(Eq. 5)}$$

$$H_2(g) + Cl_2(g) \rightarrow 2\,HCl(g) \qquad \text{(Eq. 6)}$$

Type II: Decomposition Reactions

A **decomposition reaction** occurs when a compound breaks apart to form two or more products. Equation 7 shows a generalized example, while Equations 8–10 give specific examples.

$$AB \rightarrow A + B \qquad \text{(Eq. 7)}$$

$$2\,HgO(s) \rightarrow 2\,Hg(l) + O_2(g) \qquad \text{(Eq. 8)}$$

$$BaCO_3(s) \rightarrow BaO(s) + CO_2(g) \qquad \text{(Eq. 9)}$$

$$2\,PbO_2(s) \rightarrow 2\,PbO(s) + O_2(g) \qquad \text{(Eq. 10)}$$

Type III: Single Displacement Reactions

When one element displaces another element from a compound, we call the process a **single displacement reaction**. Equation 11 shows a generalized example, and Equations 12 and 13 show specific examples.

$$A + BC \rightarrow AC + B \qquad \text{(Eq. 11)}$$

$$Sn(s) + 2\,AgNO_3(aq) \rightarrow Sn(NO_3)_2(aq) + 2\,g(s) \qquad \text{(Eq. 12)}$$

$$2\,Al(s) + 6\,HNO_3(aq) \rightarrow 2\,Al(NO_3)_3(aq) + 3\,H_2(g) \qquad \text{(Eq. 13)}$$

When we write (aq) after the formula of an ionic compound, we mean that the ions are individually solvated by water. We could rewrite Equation 12 as Equation 14 to show the solvation of the ions involved:

$$Sn(s) + 2\,Ag^+(aq) + 2\,NO_3{}^-(aq) \rightarrow Sn^{2+}(aq) + 2\,NO_3{}^-(aq) + 2\,Ag(s) \qquad \text{(Eq. 14)}$$

Equation 14 is the **complete ionic equation** for the reaction. Note that the solvated nitrate ion ($NO_3{}^-$) appears on both sides of Equation 14. Therefore it is not directly involved in the chemical reaction. We call such ions **spectator ions**. Thus, Equation 14 may be rewritten with the $NO_3{}^-$ ion omitted, as in Equation 15.

$$Sn(s) + 2\,Ag^+(aq) \rightarrow Sn^{2+}(aq) + 2\,Ag(s) \qquad \text{(Eq. 15)}$$

Equation 15 is the **net ionic equation** for this reaction.

Type IV: Double Displacement, Double Replacement, or Metathesis Reactions

A **double displacement reaction** occurs when atoms or ions in two or more different substances change places to form new compounds. One of the new compounds formed is usually either a solid, called a **precipitate**, a slightly dissociated compound, such as H_2O, or a gas. A double displacement reaction involving the formation of a precipitate is often called a **precipitation reaction**. Equation 16 is a general example; Equation 17 is a specific example.

$$AB + CD \rightarrow AD + CB \qquad \text{(Eq. 16)}$$

$$Pb(NO_3)_2(aq) + 2\,NaCl(aq) \rightarrow PbCl_2(s) + 2\,NaNO_3(aq) \qquad \text{(Eq. 17)}$$

The complete and net ionic equations for the reaction in Equation 17 are shown in Equations 18 and 19, respectively.

$$Pb^{2+}(aq) + 2\,NO_3{}^-(aq) + 2\,Na^+(aq) + 2\,Cl^-(aq) \rightarrow PbCl_2(s) + 2\,Na^+(aq) + 2\,NO_3{}^-(aq) \qquad \text{(Eq. 18)}$$

Table 2 *Chemical symbols for the elements and compounds used in this experiment*

name	chemical symbol
ammonia	NH_3
ammonium carbonate	$(NH_4)_2CO_3$
carbon(IV) oxide (carbon dioxide)	CO_2
copper	Cu
copper(II) sulfate (cupric sulfate)	$CuSO_4$
copper(II) sulfate pentahydrate	$CuSO_4 \cdot 5\ H_2O$
hydrochloric acid	HCl
iron	Fe
iron(III) chloride (ferric chloride)	$FeCl_3$
lead(II) nitrate	$Pb(NO_3)_2$
magnesium	Mg
oxygen	O_2
potassium iodide	KI
sodium hydroxide	$NaOH$
sulfur	S_8

$$Pb^{2+}(aq) + 2\,Cl^-(aq) \rightarrow PbCl_2(s) \qquad \text{(Eq. 19)}$$

In this experiment, you will mix different elements and/or components in solution. In some cases, you will heat the mixtures to promote a reaction. You will observe the appearance of the reactants and of the products, and you will determine which type of reaction occurs in each case. You will also write the chemical equations for the reactions you perform. The chemical symbols for the elements and compounds you will work with are listed in Table 2.

PROCEDURE

CHEMICAL ALERT

ammonia—toxic and corrosive
ammonium carbonate—irritant
0.1 *M* copper(II) sulfate—toxic and irritant
0.1 *M* hydrochloric acid—toxic and corrosive
0.1 *M* iron(III) chloride—corrosive
0.1 *M* lead(II) nitrate—toxic, irritant, and oxidant
magnesium—flammable
0.1 *M* potassium iodide—toxic and irritant
0.1 *M* sodium hydroxide—toxic and corrosive
sulfur—irritant

CAUTION

Wear departmentally approved eye protection while doing this experiment.

  If you spill any reagent on your hands or skin, immediately wash with ample amounts of running water.

NOTE: The numbers appearing in parentheses indicate the specific lines on your Data Sheet on which the indicated data should be entered.

I. Reacting Mg with HCl Solution

1. Transfer a 0.5-cm piece of Mg ribbon to the bottom of a clean test tube. Record on your Data Sheet your description of the appearance of the Mg (1).

CAUTION

The gas produced by the reaction of Mg and HCl solution is flammable. Be sure that there are no Bunsen burner flames in the area where you are performing this reaction.

---

2. Measure 2 mL of 0.1M HCl solution in a 10-mL graduated cylinder. Record on your Data Sheet your description of the appearance of the HCl solution (2).

   Transfer the HCl solution to the test tube containing the Mg. Observe the reaction mixture for evidence of a chemical reaction.

   Record on your Data Sheet any evidence that a chemical reaction has occurred (3).

3. Transfer the contents of your test tube to the container specified by your laboratory instructor and labeled "Discarded Mg–HCl Reaction Mixtures."

NOTE: Your laboratory instructor will tell you whether or not you should complete Step 4 before proceeding to Step 5.

---

4. Write on your Data Sheet the complete and net ionic equations for the reaction of Mg with HCl solution (4, 5). Indicate which of the four general reaction types is represented by this reaction (6).

II. Reacting Pb(NO$_3$)$_2$ Solution with KI Solution

CAUTION

Lead nitrate and KI solutions are toxic. Immediately notify your laboratory instructor if any solution spills.

If these solutions are not dispensed from a container equipped with a Pasteur pipet or other dropper, your laboratory instructor will describe and demonstrate a satisfactory method for dispensing them.

---

5. Transfer 10 drops of 0.1M Pb(NO$_3$)$_2$ solution into a clean test tube. Record on your Data Sheet your description of the appearance of the Pb(NO$_3$)$_2$ solution (7).

6. Record on your Data Sheet your description of the appearance of the 0.1M KI solution (8).

7. Using a clean Pasteur or Beral pipet, transfer 2 drops of 0.1M KI solution into the test tube containing the Pb(NO$_3$)$_2$ solution. Record on your Data Sheet your description of the appearance of the reaction mixture (9).

8. Transfer the reaction mixture in the test tube into the waste container specified by your laboratory instructor and labeled "Discarded

Pb(NO$_3$)$_2$–Kl Reaction Mixtures." Rinse the test tube with 5 mL tap water three times, and then once with 5 mL of distilled or deionized water. Transfer rinsings to the waste container.

NOTE: Your laboratory instructor will tell you whether or not you should complete Step 9 before proceeding to Step 10.

---

9. Write on your Data Sheet the complete and net ionic equations for the reaction of Pb(NO$_3$)$_2$ solution with KI solution (10, 11). Indicate which of the four general reaction types is represented by this reaction (12).

III. Heating Steel Wool (Fe) with S$_8$

10. Transfer to a porcelain crucible enough flattened steel wool to cover the crucible bottom. Record on your Data Sheet your description of the appearance of the steel wool (Fe) (13).

11. Sprinkle the amount of powdered S$_8$ that fills the end of a microspatula over the Fe (steel wool) in the crucible. Rinse the microspatula with distilled water and dry.

    Record on your Data Sheet your description of the appearance of the S$_8$ (14).

CAUTION ⚠

Do Step 12 in a fume hood. The fumes from burning S$_8$ are toxic and irritating. Avoid inhaling the fumes.

---

12. Working inside a fume hood, carefully place the crucible and its contents in a wire triangle resting on a ring attached to a ring stand, as shown in Figure 1. Cover the crucible with the crucible cover.

13. Still inside the fume hood, strongly heat the Fe–S$_8$ mixture from beneath with the flame of a Bunsen burner for 5 min. Using crucible tongs, carefully remove the crucible cover and look for evidence of unreacted S$_8$ in the crucible. If you find unreacted S$_8$, reheat the crucible for a minute or two. Check again for unreacted S$_8$. Stop heating when all visible evidence of unreacted S$_8$ has disappeared. Allow the crucible and its contents to cool to room temperature.

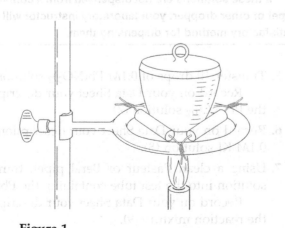

Figure 1
Positioning a crucible in a wire triangle

14. Using gentle pressure from a glass stirring rod, crush the reaction product. Observe the appearance of the reaction product. Record on your Data Sheet your description of the appearance of the reaction product (15).

15. Transfer the reaction product from the crucible into the container specified by your laboratory instructor and labeled "Discarded Fe–S_8 Reaction Products." Rinse the crucible with tap water, and dry the crucible.

NOTE: Your laboratory instructor will tell you whether or not you should complete Step 16 before proceeding to Step 17.

---

16. Write on your Data Sheet the chemical equation for the reaction of Fe and S_8 (16). Indicate which of the four general reaction types is represented by Fe and S reacting (17).

IV. Heating CuSO$_4$ · 5 H$_2$O

17. Transfer the amount of $CuSO_4 \cdot 5 H_2O$ that fills the end of a clean, dry microspatula to the bottom of a clean, dry test tube.
    Record on your Data Sheet your description of the appearance of the $CuSO_4 \cdot 5 H_2O$ (18).

18. Grasp the test tube containing $CuSO_4 \cdot 5 H_2O$ with a test tube holder. Holding the test tube at a 45° angle from the vertical, as shown in Figure 2, strongly heat the bottom of the test tube in a Bunsen burner flame. Carefully observe both the solid and the test tube walls near the open end of the test tube.

19. Record on your Data Sheet your description of the solid remaining at the bottom of the test tube and of the inside wall of the test tube (19, 20).

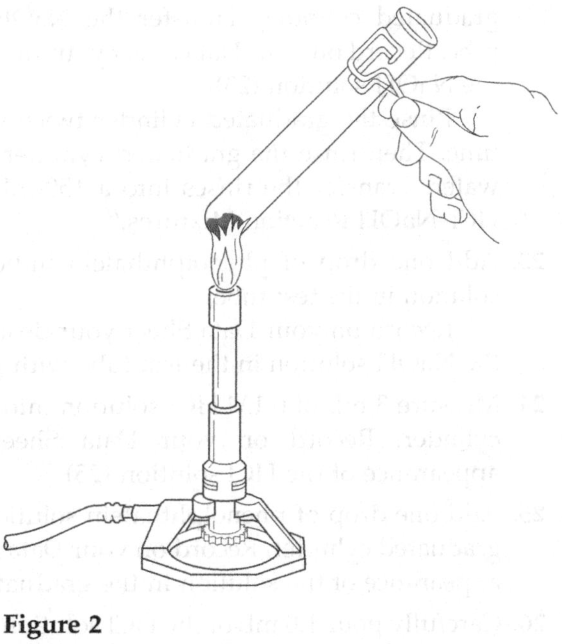

Figure 2
Heating CuSO$_4$ · 5H$_2$O in a test tube

20. Transfer the test tube contents into the container specified by your laboratory instructor and labeled "Discarded $CuSO_4 \cdot 5H_2O$ Reaction Products." Rinse the test tube twice using 5 mL of tap water each time. Then, rinse the test tube once with 5 mL of distilled water. Transfer the rinses into a 150-mL beaker labeled "Discarded $CuSO_4 \cdot 5H_2O$ Rinses."

    Transfer the contents of the "Discarded $CuSO_4 \cdot 5H_2O$ Rinses" beaker to the container specified by your laboratory instructor and labeled "Discarded $CuSO_4 \cdot 5H_2O$ Rinses." Rinse the beaker with 10 mL of tap water and pour these rinses into the drain, diluting with a large amount of running water.

NOTE: Your laboratory instructor will tell you whether or not you should complete Step 21 before proceeding to Step 22.

---

21. Write on your Data Sheet the chemical equation for the reaction of $CuSO_4 \cdot 5H_2O$ when heated (21). Indicate which of the four general reaction types is represented by this reaction (22).

V. Reacting HCl Solution with NaOH Solution

CAUTION

Both NaOH and HCl solutions are toxic and corrosive, and they can cause skin burns. Prevent contact with your eyes, skin, and clothing. Do not ingest these solutions. If you spill either solution, immediately notify your laboratory instructor.

NOTE: Phenolphthalein solution is an acid–base indicator that is red in the presence of excess hydroxide ion, OH^-, and colorless in the presence of excess H^+ ion.

---

22. Measure 2 mL of $0.1M$ NaOH solution into the rinsed 10-mL graduated cylinder. Transfer the NaOH solution into a clean test tube. Record on your Data Sheet your description of the appearance of the NaOH solution (23).

    Rinse the graduated cylinder twice with 5 mL of tap water each time. Then rinse the graduated cylinder once with 5 mL of distilled water. Transfer the rinses into a 150-mL beaker labeled "Discarded HCl–NaOH Reaction Mixtures."

23. Add one drop of phenolphthalein indicator solution to the NaOH solution in the test tube.

    Record on your Data Sheet your description of the appearance of the NaOH solution in the test tube with phenolphthalein added (24).

24. Measure 3 mL of $0.1M$ HCl solution into the rinsed 10-mL graduated cylinder. Record on your Data Sheet your description of the appearance of the HCl solution (25).

25. Add one drop of phenolphthalein solution to the HCl solution in the graduated cylinder. Record on your Data Sheet your description of the appearance of the solution in the graduated cylinder (26).

26. Carefully pour 1.0 mL of the HCl solution from the graduated cylinder into the test tube containing the NaOH solution. Use a Pasteur or Beral

pipet to add the remaining 2.0 mL of HCl solution dropwise from the graduated cylinder until you see a color change in the solution in the test tube.

Record on your Data Sheet the evidence you have that a reaction has occurred (27).

27. Pour the test tube contents into the "Discarded HCl–NaOH Reaction Mixtures" beaker. Rinse the test tube twice with 5 mL of tap water each time. Then, rinse the test tube with 5 mL of distilled water. Pour the rinses into the labeled beaker.

Rinse the graduated cylinder twice with 5 mL of tap water each time. Then rinse the graduated cylinder once with 5 mL of distilled water. Pour the rinses into the "Discarded HCl–NaOH Reaction Mixtures" beaker.

Transfer the contents of the "Discarded HCl–NaOH Reaction Mixtures" beaker to the container specified by your laboratory instructor and labeled "Discarded HCl–NaOH Reaction Mixtures." Rinse the beaker with 10 mL of tap water and pour the rinse into the drain, diluting with a large amount of running water.

NOTE: Your laboratory instructor will tell you whether or not you should complete Step 28 before proceeding to Step 29.

---

28. Write on your Data Sheet the complete and net ionic equations for the reaction of NaOH solution with HCl solution (28, 29). Indicate which of the four general reaction types is represented by this reaction (30).

VI. Heating Cu with Atmospheric O_2

NOTE: Your laboratory instructor will describe and demonstrate the adjustment of a Bunsen burner flame that is necessary to achieve an oxidizing flame.

---

29. Obtain enough Cu mesh to sparsely cover the bottom of a crucible. Record on your Data Sheet your description of the appearance of the Cu mesh (31).

30. Position the crucible in a wire triangle as shown in Figure 1, but *do not* use a crucible cover. Heat the crucible and its contents until the crucible bottom is glowing red. Remove the heat, and allow the crucible and its contents to cool to room temperature.

31. Record on your Data Sheet your description of the appearance of the Cu mesh after it has been heated and cooled to room temperature (32).

32. Dispose of the Cu mesh in the container specified by your laboratory instructor and labeled "Used Cu Mesh."

NOTE: Your laboratory instructor will tell you whether or not you should complete Step 33 before proceeding to Step 34.

---

33. Write on your Data Sheet the chemical equation for the reaction of Cu with atmospheric O_2 (33). Indicate which of the four general reaction types is represented by this reaction (34).

VII. Reacting CuSO₄ Solution with Steel Wool (Fe)

34. Obtain an amount of steel wool (Fe) equivalent to the volume of a pencil eraser. Use a clean, dry glass stirring rod to carefully slide the steel wool to the bottom of a clean, dry test tube.
    Record on your Data Sheet your description of the appearance of the steel wool (Fe) (35).

35. Measure 2 mL of $0.1M$ $CuSO_4$ solution into the rinsed 10-mL graduated cylinder. Record on your Data Sheet your description of the appearance of the $CuSO_4$ solution (36).
    Transfer the $CuSO_4$ solution into the test tube containing the steel wool (Fe).

36. Observe the appearance of the steel wool (Fe) and the surrounding solution.
    Record on your Data Sheet your description of the appearance of the steel wool (Fe) and $CuSO_4$ solution after the reaction has occurred (37, 38).

37. Dispose of the $CuSO_4$ solution in the container specified by your laboratory instructor and labeled "Discarded $CuSO_4$ Solutions." Use your stirring rod to carefully remove the steel wool from the test tube. Place the steel wool in the container specified by your laboratory instructor and labeled "Discarded Steel Wool."

NOTE: Your laboratory instructor will tell you whether or not you should complete Step 38 before proceeding to Step 39.

---

38. Write on your Data Sheet the complete and net ionic equations for the reaction of $CuSO_4$ solution with Fe (39, 40). Indicate which of the four general reaction types is represented by this reaction (41).

VIII. Reacting FeCl₃ Solution with NaOH Solution

39. Obtain 1 mL of $0.1M$ $FeCl_3$ solution in the rinsed 10-mL graduated cylinder and transfer the solution into a clean test tube. Rinse the graduated cylinder twice, using 5 mL of tap water each time, and then rinse once with 5 mL of distilled water. Transfer the rinses into a 150-mL beaker labeled "Discarded $FeCl_3$–NaOH Reaction Mixtures."
    Record on your Data Sheet your description of the appearance of the $FeCl_3$ solution (42).

40. Transfer 1 mL of $0.1M$ NaOH solution into the rinsed 10-mL graduated cylinder. Record on your Data Sheet your description of the appearance of the NaOH solution (43).

41. Transfer the NaOH solution from the graduated cylinder into the test tube containing the $FeCl_3$ solution. Rinse the graduated cylinder twice, using 5 mL of tap water each time, and once with 5 mL of distilled water. Transfer the rinses into the "Discarded $FeCl_3$– NaOH Reaction Mixtures" beaker.
    Record on your Data Sheet your description of the appearance of the reaction mixture (44).

42. Transfer the reaction mixture in the test tube into the "Discarded $FeCl_3$–NaOH Reaction Mixtures" beaker. Rinse the test tube three times, using 5 mL of tap water each time and then once with 5 mL of distilled water. Transfer rinses to the discard beaker.

Transfer the contents of the "Discarded $FeCl_3$–NaOH Reaction Mixtures" beaker to the container specified by your laboratory instructor and labeled "Discarded $FeCl_3$–NaOH Reaction Mixtures." Rinse the beaker with 10 mL of tap water and pour the rinse into the drain, diluting with a large amount of running water.

NOTE: Your laboratory instructor will tell you whether or not you should complete Step 43 before proceeding to Step 44.

---

43. Write on your Data Sheet the complete and net ionic equations for the reaction of $FeCl_3$ solution with NaOH solution (45, 46). Indicate which of the four general reaction types is represented by this reaction (47).

IX. Heating $(NH_4)_2CO_3$

44. Transfer the amount of $(NH_4)_2CO_3$ that fills the end of a microspatula to the bottom of a clean, dry test tube.
    Record on your Data Sheet your description of the appearance of the $(NH_4)_2CO_3$ (48).

NOTE: Red litmus paper turns blue in the presence of bases such as ammonia, NH_3.

---

45. Place a piece of red litmus paper on a small watch glass. Moisten the litmus paper with a drop of distilled water. The moist paper will cling to the watch glass. Record on your Data Sheet your description of the appearance of the litmus paper (49).

CAUTION ⚠

Do Step 46 in a fume hood. When $(NH_4)_2CO_3$ is heated, toxic and irritating fumes are liberated. Avoid inhaling the fumes.

---

46. Grasp the test tube containing $(NH_4)_2CO_3$ with a test tube holder. Holding the test tube at a 45° angle from the vertical, as shown in Figure 2, strongly heat the bottom of the test tube in a Bunsen burner flame. Carefully observe both the solid and the test tube walls near the open end of the test tube.

47. Holding the mouth of the test tube 15 cm or 6 in. from your face, *carefully* fan the fumes coming from the test tube toward your nose, as shown in Figure 3. Note the odor of these vapors.

48. Position the watch glass and litmus paper so that the moist paper is next to the test tube mouth. Observe the color of the litmus paper.

49. Record on your Data Sheet your descriptions of: what happened to the solid $(NH_4)_2CO_3$, the inside wall of the test tube, the odor of the vapors from the test tube mouth, and the color of the moist red litmus paper after exposure to these vapors (50, 51, 52, 53).

50. Rinse the test tube twice, using 5 mL of tap water each time. Then rinse the test tube once with 5 mL of distilled water. Transfer the rinses to a 150-mL beaker labeled "Discarded $(NH_4)_2CO_3$ Reaction Rinses."
    Transfer the contents of the "Discarded $(NH_4)_2CO_3$ Reaction Rinses" beaker to the container specified by your laboratory instructor

Figure 3
Detecting odors

and labeled "Discarded $(NH_4)_2CO_3$ Reaction Rinses." Rinse the beaker with 10 mL of tap water and pour the rinse into the drain, diluting with a large amount of running water.

51. Write on your Data Sheet the chemical equation for the reaction of $(NH_4)_2CO_3$ when heated (54). Indicate which of the four general reaction types is represented by this reaction (55).

52. If you have not already done so, complete Steps 4, 9, 16, 21, 28, 33, 38, and 43.

CAUTION

Wash your hands thoroughly with soap or detergent before leaving the laboratory.

_____   _____   _____
Name   *Section*   *Date*

Data Sheet

I. Reacting Mg with HCl Solution

(1) appearance of Mg:

(2) appearance of HCl solution:

(3) evidence that a chemical reaction occurred:

(4) complete ionic equation:

(5) net ionic equation:

(6) general reaction type:

II. Reacting Pb(NO₃)₂ Solution with KI Solution

(7) appearance of the $Pb(NO_3)_2$ solution:

(8) appearance of the KI solution:

(9) appearance of the reaction mixture:

(10) complete ionic equation:

---

(11) net ionic equation:

(12) general reaction type:

III. Heating Steel Wool (Fe) with S_8

(13) appearance of the steel wool (Fe):

(14) appearance of the S_8:

(15) appearance of the reaction product:

(16) chemical equation:

(17) general reaction type:

IV. Heating $CuSO_4 \cdot 5 H_2O$

(18) appearance of the $CuSO_4 \cdot 5 H_2O$:

(19) appearance of solid after heating:

(20) appearance of the inside wall of the test tube after heating:

(21) chemical equation:

(22) general reaction type:

V. Reacting HCl Solution with NaOH Solution

(23) appearance of the NaOH solution:

(24) appearance of the NaOH solution with phenolphthalein added:

(25) appearance of the HCl solution:

(26) appearance of the solution in the graduated cylinder:

(27) evidence that a chemical reaction has occurred:

(28) complete ionic equation:

(29) net ionic equation:

(30) general reaction type:

VI. Heating Cu with Atmospheric O$_2$

(31) appearance of the unreacted Cu mesh:

(32) appearance of the Cu mesh after heating and cooling:

(33) chemical equation:

(34) general reaction type:

VII. Reacting CuSO$_4$ Solution with Steel Wool (Fe)

(35) appearance of the steel wool (Fe) before reaction:

(36) appearance of the CuSO$_4$ solution before reaction:

(37) appearance of the steel wool (Fe) after the reaction has occurred:

(38) appearance of the CuSO$_4$ solution after the reaction has occurred:

(39) complete ionic equation:

(40) net ionic equation:

(41) general reaction type:

VIII. Reacting FeCl₃ Solution with NaOH Solution

(42) appearance of the $FeCl_3$ solution:

(43) appearance of the NaOH solution:

(44) appearance of the reaction mixture:

(45) complete ionic equation:

(46) net ionic equation:

(47) general reaction type:

IX. Heating (NH₄)₂CO₃

(48) appearance of the $(NH_4)_2CO_3$:

(49) initial appearance of the moist red litmus paper:

(50) description of what happened to the solid $(NH_4)_2CO_3$ upon heating:

(51) appearance of the inside wall of the test tube after heating:

(52) description of the odor of the fumes from $(NH_4)_2CO_3$ upon heating:

(53) appearance of the moist red litmus paper after exposure to fumes:

(54) chemical equation:

(55) general reaction type:

Name		Section	Date

Pre-Laboratory Assignment

1. Briefly answer the following questions about some of the procedures you will be using in this experiment.

(1) Why would it be dangerous to perform Part I of the procedure of this experiment close to a lighted Bunsen burner?

(2) Why is it necessary to perform the reaction of Fe with S_8 solution under a fume hood?

(3) What solutions are used in Part II of the Procedure? Briefly describe the hazards associated with each of these solutions.

(4) Although the crucible is covered while heating in Part III of this experiment, why should you heat an *uncovered* crucible in Part IV?

(5) Why is it important to wash your hands before leaving the laboratory?

2. Briefly explain what is meant by each of the following terms as it relates to this experiment.

(1) precipitation reaction

(2) spectator ion

(3) the designation (aq) following the formula of a compound

(4) decomposition reaction

(5) coefficients

3. (1) Write the complete ionic equation for the double displacement reaction that occurs when aqueous solutions of barium nitrate, $Ba(NO_3)_2$, and sodium chromate (Na_2CrO_4) are mixed.

(2) Name the spectator ions in this chemical reaction.

(3) Write the net ionic equation for this reaction.

Determining Ascorbic Acid in Vitamin C Tablets

Prepared by A. L. Kemppainen, Finlandia University

PURPOSE OF THE EXPERIMENT

Introduce acid–base titrations. Determine the mass percent of ascorbic acid in a vitamin C tablet by titration with a sodium hydroxide solution of known concentration.

BACKGROUND REQUIRED

You should be familiar with basic laboratory techniques for measuring mass and volume. You should understand the concepts associated with stoichiometry and acid–base chemistry.

BACKGROUND INFORMATION

Ascorbic acid, or vitamin C, is a water-soluble vitamin found in a variety of foods. Particularly high concentrations are found in citrus fruits, tomatoes, and leafy green vegetables. Vitamin C is an unstable vitamin; it oxidizes readily and is lost during the cooking and preserving of foods.

Adequate quantities of vitamin C must be consumed for the human body to function properly. Within the human body, the primary role of vitamin C is in the production of collagen, the major protein found in connective tissues. Vitamin C also plays a role in hemoglobin synthesis and the metabolism of certain amino acids. A prolonged deficiency of ascorbic acid results in the disease scurvy.

Individual needs for ascorbic acid may vary. The Recommended Daily Allowance (RDA) for adults is 60 milligrams (mg). Since the 1970s, studies have been done to test the suggestion that vitamin C prevents or cures the common cold and cancer. Although controlled studies are inconclusive, many people ingest much larger quantities of vitamin C than the minimum RDA. This experiment involves the analysis of the vitamin C content in vitamin supplements. The acidic nature of vitamin C is the basis for this analysis.

In aqueous solution, ascorbic acid ($HC_6H_7O_6$, abbreviated HA) will react with sodium hydroxide (NaOH), a base, to produce a salt, sodium ascorbate ($NaC_6H_7O_6$, abbreviated NaA), and water (H_2O), as shown in Equation 1.

$$\underset{\text{acid}}{\text{HA}} + \underset{\text{base}}{\text{NaOH}} \rightarrow \underset{\text{salt}}{\text{NaA}} + \underset{\text{water}}{H_2O} \qquad \text{(Eq. 1)}$$

We can determine the mass percent of ascorbic acid in a sample from a vitamin C tablet by titration with a NaOH solution. A **titration** is a procedure in which we measure the volume of a solution of known concentration that is needed to completely react with the compound we are analyzing. In this experiment, we will measure the volume of NaOH solution required to neutralize all of the ascorbic acid present in the sample.

A **buret** is a piece of calibrated glassware used to accurately deliver volumes of a liquid or a solution. In this case, the buret is used to measure the amount of NaOH solution used in a titration.

We add an acid–base **indicator** to the reaction mixture to determine when the neutralization reaction is complete. The indicator changes color at the **end point** of the titration. Phenolphthalein is the indicator used in this experiment. This indicator is colorless in acidic solutions and pink in solutions containing a slight excess of base.

Example

Problem You find that your titration requires 23.44 mL of a 0.107M NaOH to neutralize 0.56 g of a vitamin C sample. What is the sample mass percent?

Solution **(1)** *Calculate the number of moles of NaOH you used in the titration.*

$$\binom{\text{moles of NaOH}}{\text{used, mol}} = \binom{\text{molarity of NaOH}}{\text{solution, mol/L}}\binom{\text{volume of NaOH}}{\text{solution, L}} \qquad \text{(Eq. 2)}$$

$$= (0.107 \text{ mol/L})(23.44 \text{ mL})\left(\frac{1 \text{ L}}{1000 \text{ ml}}\right)$$

$$= 2.51 \times 10^{-3} \text{ mol}$$

(2) *Calculate the number of moles of ascorbic acid titrated.*

$$\binom{\text{moles of ascorbic acid}}{\text{titrated, mol}} = \binom{\text{moles of NaOH}}{\text{used, mol}}\left(\frac{1 \text{ mol ascorbic acid}}{1 \text{ mol NaOH}}\right) \qquad \text{(Eq. 3)}$$

$$= (2.51 \times 10^{-3} \text{ mol NaOH})\left(\frac{1 \text{ mol ascorbic acid}}{1 \text{ mol NaOH}}\right)$$

$$= 2.51 \times 10^{-3} \text{ mol}$$

(3) *Calculate the mass of ascorbic acid in the sample.*

$$\binom{\text{mass of ascorbic acid}}{\text{in the sample, g}} = \binom{\text{moles of ascorbic acid}}{\text{titrated, mol}}\binom{\text{molar mass of}}{\text{ascorbic acid, g/mol}} \qquad \text{(Eq. 4)}$$

$$= (2.51 \times 10^{-3} \text{ mol})(176.1 \text{ g/mol})$$

$$= 0.44 \text{ g ascorbic acid}$$

(4) *Calculate the mass percent ascorbic acid in the sample.*

$$\text{mass percent, \%} = \left(\frac{\text{mass of ascorbic acid, g}}{\text{mass of sample, g}}\right)(100\%) \qquad \text{(Eq. 5)}$$

$$= \left(\frac{0.44 \text{ g}}{0.56 \text{ g}}\right)(100\%) = 79\%$$

In this Experiment

You will prepare and fill a buret and practice operating a stopcock to deliver precise volumes of solution. You will then titrate two vitamin C samples with a NaOH solution of known concentration. From the amount of NaOH solution used in the titration, you will be able to calculate how much ascorbic acid was present in the vitamin C samples. You will then compare your findings to the product label. Finally, you will safely dispose of your discarded solutions.

PROCEDURE

CAUTION

Wear departmentally approved safety goggles while doing this experiment. Many chemicals are potentially harmful. Prevent contact with your eyes, skin, and clothing. Avoid ingesting any of the reagents. If you spill any reagents, immediately inform your laboratory instructor.

NOTE:

- Record all your data on the Data and Observations sheet.
- Record sample masses to the nearest milligram (0.001 g) or to the nearest centigram (0.01 g), according to your laboratory instructor's directions.
- Your laboratory instructor will give you instructions for disposal of your discarded solutions.
- Make notes from your Pre-Laboratory discussion here.

I. Preparing the Vitamin C Samples

1. Use a mortar and pestle to crush a vitamin C tablet.
2. Obtain two clean, 250-mL Erlenmeyer flasks. Label them "1" and "2". Weigh each flask and record the masses.
3. Transfer roughly equal portions of the ground vitamin C powder to each of the two weighed flasks. Reweigh the flasks. Record the masses.

II. Preparing and Filling the Buret

4. Obtain a 50-mL buret, a buret clamp, and a support stand. Mount the buret on the support stand, using the buret clamp as shown in Figure 1 on the next page.
5. Label a 250-mL beaker "Discarded Solutions".
6. Close the stopcock of your buret. Using a short-stem funnel, partially fill the buret with distilled or deionized water from a wash bottle or small

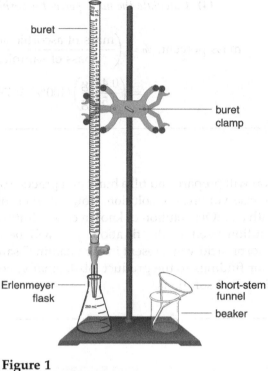

Figure 1
A titration apparatus

beaker. Open the stopcock and allow some water to drain through the tip into your Discarded Solutions beaker.

NOTE: If the buret does not drain, or if water leaks from around the stopcock, notify your laboratory instructor.

If water droplets cling to the inner walls, the buret is dirty and must be cleaned. See your laboratory instructor for directions on how to clean your buret.

---

7. Practice controlling the flow of water with the stopcock until you feel comfortable with the technique. Then empty all water from the buret. Empty your Discarded Solutions beaker into the drain.

CAUTION

NaOH solution is toxic and corrosive.   ⚠️

---

8. Obtain about 100 mL of sodium hydroxide (NaOH) solution in a clean, dry 150-mL beaker. Record the exact concentration of the NaOH solution.

9. Rinse the buret using the following procedure. Close the stopcock. Using the funnel, add 5–10 mL of NaOH solution. Remove the buret from the support stand. Holding the buret almost horizontally, rotate it so that the NaOH solution contacts the entire inner surface.

10. Clamp the buret to the support stand. Allow the NaOH solution to drain into your Discarded Solutions beaker.

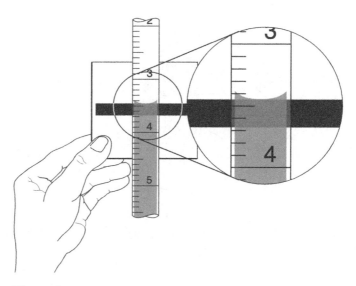

Figure 2
Reading a buret

11. With the stopcock closed and using the funnel, carefully fill the buret with NaOH solution. Add NaOH solution until it is just above the 0.00-mL line. Remove the funnel.

12. Be sure all air bubbles are removed from the buret tip. If bubbles are in the tip, remove them by opening the stopcock and allowing a small amount of NaOH solution to flow into your Discarded Solutions beaker.

13. Continue draining sufficient NaOH solution so that the bottom of the meniscus is at, or just below the 0.00-mL calibration mark. It is not necessary for the meniscus to be at 0.00 mL exactly.

NOTE: A white card with a heavy black line drawn on it can help you locate the bottom of the meniscus more readily as shown in Figure 2. Remove the funnel from the buret before reading the volume in the buret.

---

14. Read the initial buret reading. Record the reading to the nearest 0.02 mL.

III. Titrating the Vitamin C Samples

15. Add 75 mL of distilled water to flask 1. Swirl the flask.

NOTE: Do not be concerned if all of the powder does not dissolve. Tablets contain various binders and fillers, which may not dissolve in water.

CAUTION

Phenolphthalein solution is flammable and an irritant.

16. Add 3 drops of phenolphthalein solution to the flask containing the dissolved sample.

17. Place the flask under the buret as shown in Figure 1. Open the stopcock and allow about 1 mL of NaOH solution to flow into the flask at a time. Swirl the flask continuously during the titration as shown in Figure 3 on the next page.

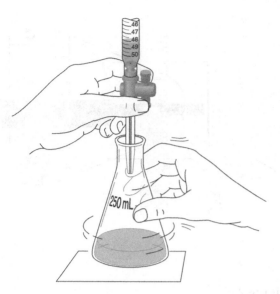

Figure 3
Positioning the buret for titration and manipulating the stopcock

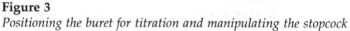

NOTE: Do not overtitrate. As the NaOH solution is added, a pink color appears where the drop of base enters the solution. The titration is near the end point when the pink streaks spread further out and disappear more slowly.

   If you add too much NaOH solution and pass beyond the pale pink end point, you must repeat the titration.

18. When you observe that the pink color takes longer to disappear, proceed slowly, adding NaOH 1 drop at a time. When 1 drop of NaOH solution causes the reaction mixture to turn pink and the pink color persists for 30 s, you have reached the end point of the titration. Stop adding NaOH solution.

19. Record the final buret reading.

20. Pour the titration mixture into the drain with a large amount of running water.

21. If necessary, refill the buret with NaOH solution. Record the initial buret reading. Do a second determination following Steps 14–19 with the vitamin C sample in flask 2.

22. When you have completed your second determination, drain the NaOH solution from your buret into the Discarded Solutions beaker. Rinse the buret with tap water. Drain the rinse water into the Discarded Solutions beaker.

23. Rinse the buret with distilled water. With the stopcock open, invert the buret and clamp to the support stand.

24. Pour any excess NaOH solution from your 150-mL beaker into the Discarded Solutions beaker. Rinse the beaker with 5–10 mL of distilled water. Pour the rinse water into the Discarded Solutions beaker.

25. Proceed with Step 26 if you are doing Part IV. If you are not doing Part IV, dispose of your Discarded Solutions as directed by your laboratory instructor.

**IV. Disposing of Your
Discarded Solutions**

CAUTION

6*M* HCl is toxic and corrosive.

26. Add 3 drops of phenolphthalein solution to the Discarded Solutions beaker. If the resulting solution is not pink, consult with your laboratory instructor.

27. If the solution is pink, add 6*M* hydrochloric acid (HCl) dropwise. Using a stirring rod, mix the solution well after each addition. Continue adding HCl until 1 drop causes the solution to become colorless. Pour the colorless solution into the drain with a large amount of running water.

CAUTION

Wash your hands thoroughly with soap or detergent before leaving the laboratory.

_____   _____   _____   _____
Name   *Partner*   *Section*   *Date*

Post-Laboratory Questions

Use the spaces provided for the answers and additional paper if necessary.

1. (a) Read the label on the vitamin C bottle. How many milligrams of ascorbic acid does the manufacturer state is in each tablet?

(b) How many milligrams of ascorbic acid did you determine were in one tablet? (mass ascorbic acid flask 1 + mass ascorbic acid flask 2)

(c) Briefly explain any differences noted between (a) and (b).

2. (a) In this experiment, what was the greatest source of error that limited the precision of your results?

(b) What could you do differently?

3. Suppose the 250-mL beaker was wet when you added the NaOH solution to it. Specifically, how would this affect your reported amount of ascorbic acid? Briefly explain your reasoning.

4. To retain the vitamin C content of fresh foods, it is better to keep the protective covering on fresh fruits and vegetables until just before eating. Briefly explain why.

_____ _____ _____ _____
Name   *Partner*   *Section*   *Date*

Data and Observations

I. Preparing the Vitamin C Samples

	determination	
	1	2
mass of empty flask, g	_____	_____
mass of flask and sample, g	_____	_____

II. Preparing and Filling the Buret

concentration of NaOH solution, *M*   _____

III. Titrating the Vitamin C Samples

initial buret reading, mL	_____	_____
final buret reading, mL	_____	_____

Calculations and Conclusions

Show your calculations for each determination in the spaces provided. Remember to include units with all calculated results.

1. Calculate the mass, in grams, of the sample titrated.

mass of sample in flask 1, g   _____

mass of sample in flask 2, g   _____

2. Calculate the volume, in liters, of NaOH solution required to neutralize the ascorbic acid.

volume of NaOH solution added to flask 1, L   _____

Volume of NaOH solution added to flask 2, L   _____

3. Calculate the number of moles of NaOH required to neutralize the ascorbic acid, using Equation 2.

moles of NaOH required in flask 1, mol   _____

moles of NaOH required in flask 2, mol   _____

4. Calculate the number of moles of ascorbic acid titrated, using Equation 3.

moles of ascorbic acid titrated in flask 1, mol   _____

moles of ascorbic acid titrated in flask 2, mol   _____

5. Calculate the mass, in grams, of ascorbic acid neutralized, using Equation 4.

mass of ascorbic acid neutralized in flask 1, g   _____

mass of ascorbic acid neutralized in flask 2, g   _____

6. Calculate the mass percent ascorbic acid in each sample, using Equation 5.

mass percent of ascorbic acid in flask 1, %   _____

mass percent of ascorbic acid in flask 2, %   _____

7. Calculate the average mass percent ascorbic acid in the tablet using Equation 6.

$$\text{averager mass percent, \%} = \frac{(\text{mass percent flask 1} + \text{mass percent flask 2})}{2} \qquad (\text{Eq. 6})$$

average mass percent ascorbic acid, %   _____

| Name | Partner | Section | Date |

Pre-Laboratory Assignment

1. What are the hazards associated with sodium hydroxide (NaOH) solution?

2. (a) What buret reading should you record when the liquid level is as shown in Figure 2?

(b) How will you recognize the end point of your titration?

3. A student collected the following data in the laboratory.

mass of flask, g	52.87
mass of flask and sample, g	53.42
concentration of NaOH solution, M	0.101
initial buret reading, mL	0.50
final buret reading, mL	23.78

(a) What is the mass, in grams, of the sample?

(b) What volume, in liters, of NaOH solution was used in the titration?

(c) How many moles of NaOH solution were used in the titration?

(d) How many moles of ascorbic acid were neutralized?

(e) How many grams of ascorbic acid is this?

(f) What is the mass percent ascorbic acid in the sample?

Molecular Models: Lewis Dot Formulas, VSEPR Theory, and Valence Bond Theory

OBJECTIVE To construct models of compounds and to use Lewis Dot formulas and the Valence Shell Electron Pair Repulsion (VSEPR) Theory to predict shapes and polarity of small molecules and polyatomic ions.

CONCEPT TO BE TESTED Molecular models are useful in predicting and explaining the properties of substances. Models may take the form of two dimensional Lewis dot diagrams or three dimensional ball and stick models.

TEXT REFERENCES (1) Whitten, Davis, Peck, Stanley: 7.1, 7.3 - 7.9, 8.1 - 8.15 (2) Kotz, Treichel: 9.1, 9.4, 9.7, 9.9 - 9.10 (3) Masterton, Hurley: 7.1 - 7.4 (4) Moore, Stanitski, Jurs: 8.9, 9.1 - 9.4

LABORATORY MANUAL REFERENCES (1) Do not perform this experiment until you clearly understand how to handle any chemical or procedural hazards in a safe manner so that you prevent injury to yourself or others. Study Chemical Safety and Rules, pp 29-31 (2)The material covered in Background IV: Periodic Table and Periodicity are basic to the understanding of this experiment. (3) App. B - Formulas, Names and Charges of Some Common Ions, App. G - Molecular and Ionic Chemical Equations,.

INTRODUCTION

Chemists use large-sized models of molecules, atoms and bonds to represent particles that are too small to see with the human eye. These macro-sized models are useful for visualizing the physical arrangements of atoms in molecules and polyatomic ions. These models also aid in understanding properties, such as the polarity of some molecules, and the reactivity and interaction of atoms in molecules. Molecular models are ball and stick sets in which each ball of a different color represents atoms of a different element. (Candy gum drops or styrofoam balls and toothpicks may also be used instead.)

A basic concept of the atomic theory is that the chemical and physical properties of a substance are determined by the distribution of outer shell (highest n value) electrons in its atoms and by the spatial arrangement of these atoms in the structure of the substance. Lewis Dot formulas are two dimensional representations that use the arrangement of outer shell electrons to give basic information on the three dimensional shapes of molecules and polyatomic ions.

Experimental techniques such as x-ray or neutron defraction in crystals, ultraviolet, infrared, Raman and microwave spectroscopy, and dipole moment measurements furnish information on the relative positions or geometric arrangement of atoms in real molecules and in polyatomic ions. Experimental data on shapes and polarity agree very closely with shapes and polarity predicted from models for simple molecules and ions.

The following rules and procedures are given as a guide in drawing Lewis Electron Dot Formulas.

A. Lewis Electron Dot Formula

1) Rules for Arrangement of Molecular Skeleton Structure

1. a. For small molecules and polyatomic ions, place the element with the lowest electronegativity in the center and arrange the more electronegative atoms around it. Hydrogen is never the central atom.

CS_2 $[S \quad C \quad S]^0$ CO_3^{2-} $\left[\begin{array}{c} O \\ O \quad C \quad O \end{array}\right]^{2-}$

   b. Oxygen atoms do not bond to each other except in (1) O_2 and O_3 molecules and (2) peroxides, O_2^{2-} and superperoxides, O_2^-.

2. The hydrogen atoms in oxyacids are usually bonded to oxygen atoms which in turn are bonded to the less electronegative central atom.

HNO_3 $\left[\begin{array}{c} O \\ H \quad O \quad N \\ O \end{array}\right]^0$ H_2SO_4 $\left[\begin{array}{c} O \\ H \quad O \quad S \quad O \quad H \\ O \end{array}\right]^0$

2) Steps for Arrangement of Electron Dots*

1. Determine the number of electrons that will be needed (N) to satisfy each atom. Usually all atoms need 8 electrons each except hydrogen, which needs 2 electrons.

   CS_2 $N = 8$ (for the C)+ 2 (8) (for each S) = 24e$^-$

   CO_3^{2-} $N = 8$ (for the C)+ 3(8) (for each O) = 32 e$^-$

2. Determine the number of valence electrons available (A) from each atom. For polyatomic ions, *subtract* one electron for each *positive* charge and *add* one electron for each negative charge.

   CS_2 $A = 4$ (for C) + 2(6) (for each S) = 16 e$^-$

   CO_3^{2-} $A = 4$ (for C) + 3(6) (for each O) + 2 (for −2 charge) = 24 e$^-$

3. Calculate the number of electrons shared (S) in the molecule. $S = N - A$

   CS_2 $S = 24 - 16 = 8$ e$^-$

   CO_3^{2-} $S = 32 - 24 = 8$ e$^-$

4. Place the S electrons in pairs between the central atom and each bonded atom. If all the shared electrons (Step 3) have not been used, insert pairs to

   $S::C::S$ $\left[\begin{array}{c} O \\ O:\ddot{C}::O \end{array}\right]^{2-}$

   make double bonds. Do not exceed the number of covalent bonds that the *outer* atom can form. (H and Gp VII = 1, Gp VI = 2, Gp V = 3, Gp IV = 4)

5. Calculate the number of the available electrons which are not shared (NS) in the molecule   (NS) = A – S.

   CS_2 (NS) = 16 – 8 = 8 e$^-$

   CO_3^{2-} (NS) = 24 – 8 = 16 e$^-$

6. Use the nonshared electrons (Step 5) in pairs to complete the number of electrons each atom *needs*.

   $\ddot{S}::C::\ddot{S}$ $\left[\begin{array}{c} :\ddot{O}: \\ :\ddot{O}:\ddot{C}::\ddot{O} \end{array}\right]^{2-}$

* There are compounds that can not be represented by these steps for Lewis Dot Formulas. The central atom may have less than 8 electrons (BF_3) or more than 8 electrons (PCl_5, SF_6, XeF_4, etc). For most of these compounds, the central atom and each outer atom are bonded by single bonds consisting of one electron from the central atom and one electron from the outer atom. If there are any extra electrons on the central atom, they are grouped as unshared pairs on the central atom.

Exercise: Circle each pair of electrons that is shaired between two atoms below.

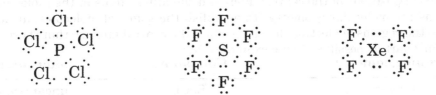

B. Theories of Electronic Geometry and Molecular Shapes

1) Valence Shell Electron Pair Repulsion (VSEPR) Theory

The VSEPR theory states that regions of high electron density will arrange them-selves as far apart as possible around the central atom. One region of high electron density is counted for each single, double, or triple bond, or for each unshared pair of electrons (lone pair) on the central atom. In the examples shown above, CS_2 has two regions, CO_3^{2-} has three regions, PCl_5 has five regions, SF_6 and XeF_4 have six regions. The following electronic geometries are expected for these numbers of re-gions of high electron density.

regions	2	3	4	5	6
geometry	Linear	Trigonal	Tetrahedral planar	Trigonal	Octahedral bipyramidal

2) The Valence Bond Theory

The Valence Bond Theory proposes that the higher energy atomic orbitals on the central atom hybridize (mix) when atoms approach for bonding. Electrons in orbitals on the central atom are "promoted" to higher orbitals which were not used in the ground state. These orbitals can accept electrons from other atoms. The atomic orbitals that are hybridized give new shapes that are different from the original atomic orbitals. When atoms bond through the new hybridized orbitals, the molecule will have a characteristic shape that depends on the atomic orbitals used in hybridization.

In methane, CH_4, carbon is the "central atom" and hydrogen is the "other atoms."

Electron Orbitals For Carbon

	1s	2s	2p	3s	3p	
ground state	↑↓	↑↓	↑ ↑ __	__	__ __ __	
promoted state	↑↓	↑	↑ ↑ ↑			(1 - s, 3 - p orbitals)
bonded hybrid state	↑↓	↑↓ ↑↓ ↑↓ ↑↓				four sp³ hybrid orbitals (tetrahedral)

The shapes of common kinds of hybrid orbitals follow:

sp	linear	dsp^2	square planar
sp^2	trigonal planar	sp^3d or dsp^3	trigonal bipyramidal
sp^3*	tetrahedral	sp^3d^2 or d^2sp^3	octahedral

* This hybridization is not used for elements in Gp V and Gp VI except in period 2. For these elements in higher periods, only atomic "p" orbitals are used in bonding. These are at right angles to each other. This still accounts for the molecular shapes of trigonal pyramidal Gp V and bent (angular) Gp IV molecules.

C.   Molecular Geometry (shape)

The relative positions of the central atom and the other atoms in the molecule can be described as the molecular geometry. To establish the shape of molecules, attach the other atoms to the regions of electron density around the central atom so that these other atoms are as far apart as possible. Some examples follow.

Electronic geometry	Compound	Molecular geometry

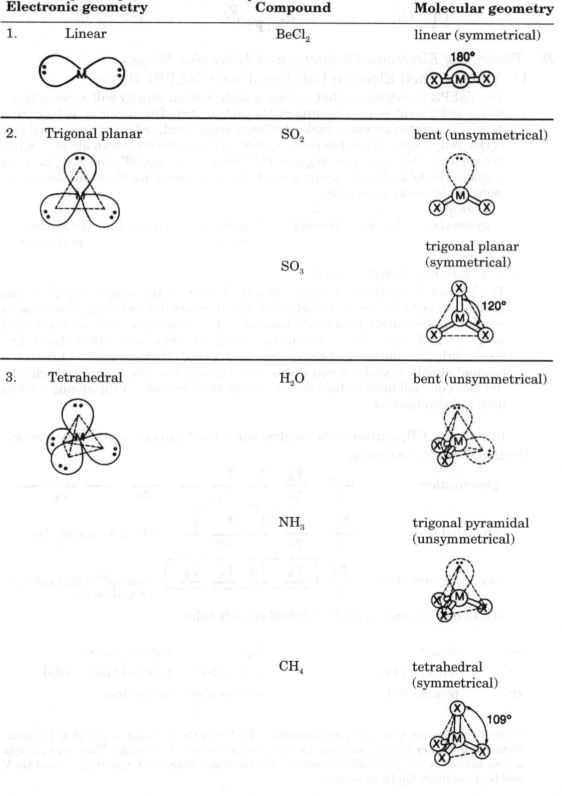

1. Linear	$BeCl_2$	linear (symmetrical)
2. Trigonal planar	SO_2	bent (unsymmetrical)
	SO_3	trigonal planar (symmetrical)
3. Tetrahedral	H_2O	bent (unsymmetrical)
	NH_3	trigonal pyramidal (unsymmetrical)
	CH_4	tetrahedral (symmetrical)

Electronic geometry	Compound	Molecular geometry
4. Trigonal bipyramidal	XeF_2	linear (symmetrical)
	ClF_3	t-shaped (unsymmetrical)
	SCl_4	seesaw (unsymmetrical)
	PCl_5	trigonal bipyramidal (symmetrical)
5. Octahedral	XeF_4	square planar (symmetrical)
	IF_5	square pyramidal (unsymmetrical)
	SCl_6	octahedral (symmetrical)

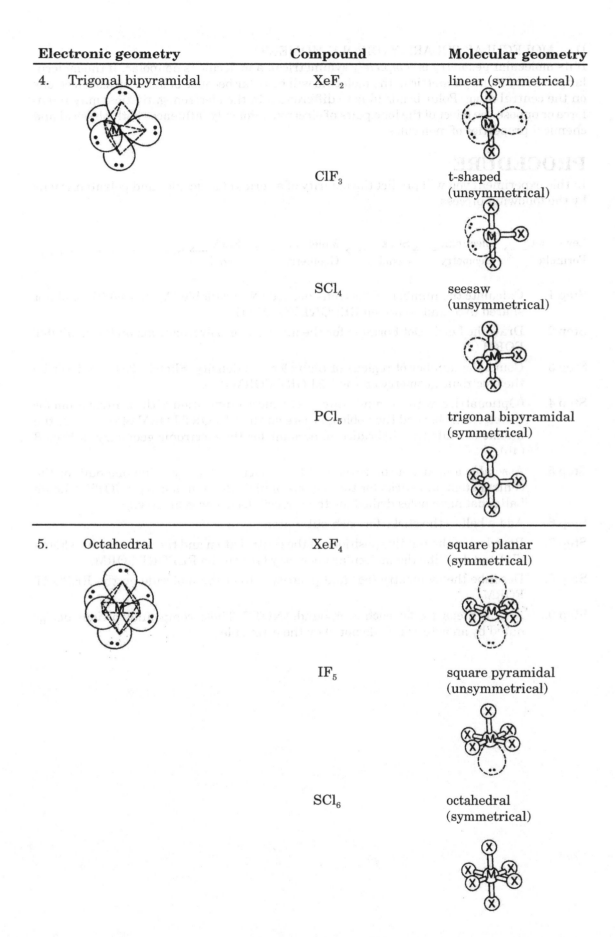

D.   MOLECULAR POLARITY (DIPOLE MOMENT)

If its molecular geometry is *completely* symmetrical, a molecule is nonpolar. If the molecular geometry is unsymmetrical, the molecule will be polar because of lone pairs of electrons on the central atom. Polar bonds (due to differences in the electronegativities) may re-enforce or oppose the effect of the lone pairs of electrons. Polarity influences both physical and chemical properties of molecules.

PROCEDURE

In this experiment you will predict the polarity of a series of molecules and polyatomic ions by the following process:

Lewis Dot Formula $\longrightarrow$ Electronic Geometry $\longrightarrow$ Stick model $\longrightarrow$ Molecular Geometry $\longrightarrow$ Stick model $\longrightarrow$ Symmetry $\longrightarrow$ Polarity

Step 1.   Calculate the number of electrons needed (N), available (A), shared (S), and not shared (*NS*) and record on REPORT FORM (1).

Step 2.   Draw the Lewis Dot Formula for the molecule or polyatomic ion on the REPORT FORM (2).

Step 3.   Count the number of regions of high electron density. Sketch (3a) and describe the electronic geometry on the REPORT FORM (3b).

Step 4.   (Optional) Draw the ground state electronic configuration of the central atom for the electrons beyond the noble gas core on the REPORT FORM (4a). Predict the atomic obritals that hybridize to account for the electronic geometry in Step 3 (4b).

Step 5.   Assemble a model of the regions of high electron density using one ball for the central atom and sticks for the regions of high electron density. (NOTE: Choose balls that have holes drilled for the correct electronic geometry.)

Step 6.   Add a ball to the sticks for each outer atom.

Step 7.   Based upon the relative positions of the central atom and the outer atoms, sketch (7a) and describe the molecular geometry (7b) on the REPORT FORM.

Step 8.   Describe the symmetry (8a) and polarity (8b) of the molecule on the REPORT FORM.

Step 9.   Repeat Steps 1-8 for each compound. (NOTE: Those compounds or ions designated by an asterisk (*) do not obey the octet rule.)

Name _____   Lab Instructor _____

Date _____   Lab Section _____

Prelab Questions

1. Write the ground state electronic configurations for the following atoms or ions. Arrange the electrons in increasing major energy levels. Diagram the electronic configuration for electrons beyond the noble gas core for each particle.

V	$1s^2\,2s^2\,2p^6\,3s^2\,3p^6\,4s^2\,3d^3$	[V] $\uparrow\ \ \uparrow\ \ \uparrow\ \ \_\ \ \_\quad \uparrow\downarrow$
		$\qquad\qquad\quad$ 3d $\qquad\qquad$ 4s
B		
B^{3+}		
Se		
Se^{2-}		
Sn		
Sn^{2+}		
Sn^{4+}		

2. Write the dot formula for the folowing atoms or ions.

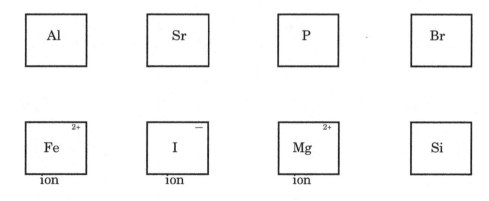

Al	Sr	P	Br

Fe^{2+}	I^{-}	Mg^{2+}	Si
ion	ion	ion	

3.   What is the electronic geometry about a central atom which has
     (a) two regions of electron density

     (b) five regions of electron density

4.   What is the molecular geometry about a central atom which has the number of electron density regions and the number of attached atoms indicated below?

	no. of electron density regions	no. attached atom	molecular geometry
example:	3	2	bent
a.	5	4	
b.	4	3	
c.	6	5	
d.	5	2	
e.	6	4	

Formula	Dot Requirement	Dot Formula	Electronic Geometry	Molecular Geometry	(Circle one)
BF_4^-	(1) N = 8 + 5(8) = 40 A = 3 + 4(7) + = 32 8 S = Not shared = 24	(2) $\left[\begin{array}{c} :\ddot{F}: \\ :\ddot{F}:B:\ddot{F}: \\ :\ddot{F}: \end{array} \right]^-$	(3a) (3b) tetrahedral (4a) $\underset{1s}{\uparrow\downarrow} \quad \underset{2s}{\uparrow} \quad \underset{2p}{\underline{\ \ }\ \underline{\ \ }\ \underline{\ \ }}$	(7a) (7b) Tetrahedral	(8a) Symmetrical (Y) N (8b) Polar Y (N) (4b) hybridization sp^3
H_2Se	(1) N = A = S = Not shared =	(2)	(3a) (3b) (4a)	(7a) (7b)	(8a) Symmetrical Y N (8b) Polar Y N (4b) hybridization
HCN	(1) N = A = S = Not shared =	(2)	(3a) (3b) (4a)	(7a) (7b)	(8a) Symmetrical Y N (8b) Polar Y N (4b) hybridization

* Dot formula is an exception to rules.

Formula	Dot Requirement	Dot Formula	Electronic Geometry	Molecular Geometry	(Circle one)
TeO_2	(1) N = A = S = Not shared =	(2)	(3a) (3b) (4a)	(7a) (7b)	(8a) Symmetrical Y N (8b) Polar Y N (4b) hybridization
SeO_3^{2-}	(1) N = A = S = Not shared =	(2)	(3a) (3b) (4a)	(7a) (7b)	(8a) Symmetrical Y N (8b) Polar Y N (4b) hybridization
* PF_5	(1) N = A = S = Not shared =	(2)	(3a) (3b) (4a)	(7a) (7b)	(8a) Symmetrical Y N (8b) Polar Y N (4b) hybridization

Formula	Dot Requirement	Dot Formula	Electronic Geometry	Molecular Geometry	(Circle one)
* $BeCl_2$	(1) N = A = S = Not shared =	(2)	(3a) (3b) (4a)	(7a) (7b)	(8a) Symmetrical Y N (8b) Polar Y N (4b) hybridization
PO_3^{3-}	(1) N = A = S = Not shared =	(2)	(3a) (3b) (4a)	(7a) (7b)	(8a) Symmetrical Y N (8b) Polar Y N (4b) hybridization
$CHBr_3$	(1) N = A = S = Not shared =	(2)	(3a) (3b) (4a)	(7a) (7b)	(8a) Symmetrical Y N (8b) Polar Y N (4b) hybridization

* Dot formula is an exception to rules.

Formula	Dot Requirement	Dot Formula	Electronic Geometry	Molecular Geometry	(Circle one)
$S_2O_3^{2-}$	(1) N = A = S = Not shared =	(2)	(3a) (3b) (4a)	(7a) (7b)	(8a) Symmetrical Y N (8b) Polar Y N (4b) hybridization
NO_2^-	(1) N = A = S = Not shared =	(2)	(3a) (3b) (4a)	(7a) (7b)	(8a) Symmetrical Y N (8b) Polar Y N (4b) hybridization
* BrF_3	(1) N = A = S = Not shared =	(2)	(3a) (3b) (4a)	(7a) (7b)	(8a) Symmetrical Y N (8b) Polar Y N (4b) hybridization

Formula	Dot Requirement	Dot Formula	Electronic Geometry	Molecular Geometry	(Circle one)
NH_2^-	(1) N = A = S = Not shared =	(2)	(3a) (3b) (4a)	(7a) (7b)	(8a) Symmetrical Y N (8b) Polar Y N (4b) hybridization
BrO_2^-	(1) N = A = S = Not shared =	(2)	(3a) (3b) (4a)	(7a) (7b)	(8a) Symmetrical Y N (8b) Polar Y N (4b) hybridization
* ClF_3	(1) N = A = S = Not shared =	(2)	(3a) (3b) (4a)	(7a) (7b)	(8a) Symmetrical Y N (8b) Polar Y N (4b) hybridization

* Dot formula is an exception to rules.

Formula	Dot Requirement	Dot Formula	Electronic Geometry	Molecular Geometry	(Circle one)
* ICl_3	(1) N = A = S = Not shared =	(2)	(3a) (3b) (4a)	(7a) (7b)	(8a) Symmetrical Y N (8b) Polar Y N (4b) hybridization
* SeF_4	(1) N = A = S = Not shared =	(2)	(3a) (3b) (4a)	(7a) (7b)	(8a) Symmetrical Y N (8b) Polar Y N (4b) hybridization
* XeF_4	(1) N = A = S = Not shared =	(2)	(3a) (3b) (4a)	(7a) (7b)	(8a) Symmetrical Y N (8b) Polar Y N (4b) hybridization

Quantitatively Determining the Acid Content of Fruit Juices

Prepared by Andrew W. Zanella, Claremont McKenna College, Pitzer College, and Scripps College

PURPOSE OF THE EXPERIMENT

Determine the acid content of various fruit juices by titration with standard sodium hydroxide solution.

BACKGROUND INFORMATION

The sour taste of many fruit juices is due in large part to the presence of acids. Citric acid, $C_3H_5O(COOH)_3$, is one of several acids present in these juices. Citric acid reacts with sodium hydroxide (NaOH), a base, as shown in Equation 1.

$$C_3H_5O(COOH)_3(aq) + 3\,NaOH(aq) \rightarrow C_3H_5O(COO)_3Na_3(aq) + 3\,H_2O(l) \qquad \text{(Eq. 1)}$$

Equation 1 describes a **neutralization reaction**, in which an acid and base react to form water and a type of ionic compound called a **salt**. In the neutralization of $C_3H_5O(COOH)_3$, the salt is sodium citrate, $C_3H_5O(COO)_3Na_3$. Although various acids are found in different amounts in different fruit juices, for the purposes of this experiment, we will assume that the acid content of these juices consists entirely of $C_3H_5O(COOH)_3$.

We can determine the amount of acid in a given volume of fruit juice by titrating the juice with a standard NaOH solution. A **standard solution** is a solution of known concentration. We frequently express the concentration of a standard solution in terms of molarity. The **molarity** (mol L^{-1}, or M) of a solution is the number of moles of solute per liter of solution, as expressed by Equation 2.

$$\text{molarity, } M = \frac{\text{number of moles of solute}}{\text{volume of solution, L}} \qquad \text{(Eq. 2)}$$

We measure the volume of NaOH solution required for the neutralization by titration. **Titration** is the measurement of the volume of a standard solution required to completely react with a measured volume or mass of the substance being analyzed. We add the standard solution from a calibrated glass tube called a **buret**. Before beginning the titration, we add an indicator to the titration mixture. An **indicator** is a substance that changes color at the point when the titration reaction is complete. In this experiment, you will use phenolphthalein as an indicator when you titrate fruit juice with NaOH solution. Phenolphthalein is a complex organic dye that is colorless in acidic solutions and pink in solutions that are slightly alkaline, or basic.

Assume that we want to determine the acidity ($C_3H_5O(COOH)_3$ content) of an orange juice sample. We find that 39.62 mL of 0.106M NaOH solution are required to titrate a 10.0-mL sample of orange juice. We determine the number of moles of NaOH required to neutralize the $C_3H_5O(COOH)_3$ from the concentration and volume of NaOH solution used in the titration, and a rearrangement of Equation 2, shown as Equation 3. Note that in part of Equation 3 the NaOH volume is converted from milliliters to liters.

$$\begin{array}{l}\text{number of moles of} \\ \text{NaOH required, mol}\end{array} = \left(\begin{array}{c}\text{volume of} \\ \text{NaOH solution} \\ \text{required, mL}\end{array}\right)\left(\frac{1\ \text{L}}{1000\ \text{mL}}\right)\left(\begin{array}{c}\text{concentration} \\ \text{of NaOH} \\ \text{solution, mol L}^{-1}\end{array}\right) \quad \text{(Eq. 3)}$$

$$= 39.62\ \text{mL}\left(\frac{1\ \text{L}}{1000\ \text{mL}}\right)\left(\frac{0.106\ \text{mol NaOH}}{1\ \text{L solution}}\right)$$

$$= 4.20 \times 10^{-3}\ \text{mol NaOH}$$

We determine the number of moles of $C_3H_5O(COOH)_3$ in the titrated juice sample using Equation 4 and the stoichiometry of the titration reaction given in Equation 1.

$$\begin{array}{l}\text{number of moles of} \\ C_3H_5O(COOH)_3,\ \text{mol}\end{array} = \left(\begin{array}{c}\text{number of moles} \\ \text{of NaOH}\end{array}\right)\left(\frac{1\ \text{mol } C_3H_5O(COOH)_3}{3\ \text{mol NaOH}}\right) \quad \text{(Eq. 4)}$$

$$= (4.20 \times 10^{-3}\ \text{mol NaOH})\left(\frac{1\ \text{mol } C_3H_5O(COOH)_3}{3\ \text{mol NaOH}}\right)$$

$$= 1.40 \times 10^{-3}\ \text{mol } C_3H_5O(COOH)_3$$

We compute the mass of $C_3H_5O(COOH)_3$ in the titrated juice sample using Equation 5. The molar mass of $C_3H_5O(COOH)_3$ is 192.12 g mol^{-1}.

$$\begin{array}{l}\text{mass of } C_3H_5O(COOH)_3 \\ \text{in sample, g}\end{array} = \left(\begin{array}{c}\text{number of moles of} \\ C_3H_5O(COOH)_3\end{array}\right)\left(\frac{192.12\ \text{g } C_3H_5O(COOH)_3}{1\ \text{mol of } C_3H_5O(COOH)_3}\right) \quad \text{(Eq. 5)}$$

$$= \left(\begin{array}{c}1.40 \times 10^{-3}\ \text{mol} \\ C_3H_5O(COOH)_3\end{array}\right)\left(\frac{192.12\ \text{g } C_3H_5O(COOH)_3}{1\ \text{mol of } C_3H_5O(COOH)_3}\right)$$

$$= 0.269\ \text{g } C_3H_5O(COOH)_3$$

For convenience in making comparisons between different juices, we determine the mass of $C_3H_5O(COOH)_3$ present in 1 mL of juice, using Equation 6.

$$\begin{array}{l}\text{mass of } C_3H_5O(COOH)_3 \\ \text{in 1 mL juice, g mL}^{-1}\end{array} = \frac{\text{mass of } C_3H_5O(COOH)_3\ \text{in sample, g}}{\text{volume of juice titrated, mL}} \quad \text{(Eq. 6)}$$

$$= \frac{0.269\ \text{g } C_3H_5O(COOH)_3}{10.0\ \text{mL juice}}$$

$$= 2.69 \times 10^{-2}\ \text{g } C_3H_5O(COOH)_3\ \text{mL}^{-1}$$

When evaluating the result of this calculation, we need to recall that we assumed that the only acid present in the juice was $C_3H_5O(COOH)_3$. This assumption is useful for comparative purposes. We would need to devise and execute a much more complex analytical scheme if we wanted to determine the exact amounts and identities of the individual acids actually present in the juice sample.

In this experiment, you will determine the number of grams of acid, assuming it is entirely $C_3H_5O(COOH)_3$, present in 1 mL of a fruit juice by titrating the juice sample with standard NaOH solution. If a variety of juice samples are available for analysis, you will be able to compare the acidities of these juices by comparing your results with those of your classmates.

PROCEDURE

CHEMICAL ALERT

0.1 *M* sodium hydroxide—toxic and corrosive

CAUTION

Wear departmentally approved eye protection while doing this experiment.

I. Preparing the Fruit Juice for Titration

NOTE: The numbers appearing in parentheses indicate the specific lines on your Data Sheet on which the indicated data should be entered.

1. Obtain 75 mL of fruit juice from your laboratory instructor in a clean, dry 150-mL beaker. Record the type of fruit juice and the code identification of the juice sample on your Data Sheet (1,2).

NOTE: If the juice has substantial amounts of pulp floating in it, filter the juice by pouring it from the beaker into another clean, dry 150-mL beaker through some glass wool placed in a conical funnel. Otherwise, the pulp tends to obscure the titration end point.

NOTE: Your laboratory instructor will tell you whether or not you should titrate any volume of juice *other than* that specified in Step 3. If it is necessary for you to dilute your juice prior to titration, your instructor will give you information concerning the appropriate calculations.

2. Label two clean, 125-mL Erlenmeyer flasks "1" and "2."

NOTE: Your laboratory instructor may suggest that you dispense your juice from a dispensing buret or a 20-mL pipet. If so, you will deliver 20.00 mL of sample, rather than 20.0 mL as mentioned in Step 3, due to the greater precision of these types of glassware.

3. Measure 20.0 mL of your juice from the beaker into a 25-mL graduated cylinder. Transfer the juice into Erlenmeyer flask 1. Record on your Data Sheet the volume of juice transferred (3).

Rinse the graduated cylinder twice, using 5 mL of distilled or deionized water each time. Transfer the rinses into Erlenmeyer flask 1.

4. Use the procedure in Step 3 to transfer a 20.0-mL juice sample to Erlenmeyer flask 2.

5. Add three drops of phenolphthalein indicator solution to the solution in each Erlenmeyer flask. Gently swirl each flask and its contents to thoroughly mix each solution.

II. Cleaning and Filling the Buret

NOTE: Your laboratory instructor will demonstrate and describe an acceptable technique for adding solutions to your buret. One such method involves placing a funnel in the top of the buret and pouring the solution into the funnel.

If you use a funnel, be sure to rinse the inner surface of the funnel with the solution you will be adding to the buret, prior to placing the funnel in the buret.

6. Holding the buret vertically, close the stopcock and fill the buret with tap water. Open the stopcock, and drain the water through the buret tip into the drain. If any water drops remain on the inner surface of the barrel, the buret is dirty and must be cleaned.

7. If the buret needs cleaning, dip a buret brush into a warm detergent solution in a 150-mL beaker. Scrub the inside buret wall. *Do not push the end of the brush below the 50-mL calibration line.*

8. Close the stopcock, and add approximately 10 mL of tap water to the buret. Open the stopcock, and drain the water through the buret tip into the drain. Repeat this procedure until you have rinsed all of the detergent from the buret.

9. Close the stopcock, and add 10 mL of distilled water to the buret. Clamp the buret to a support stand, and let the buret stand for a few minutes. Consult your laboratory instructor if the buret leaks.

10. Remove the buret from the support stand. Hold the buret almost horizontally. Carefully rotate the buret so that water contacts the entire inner surface.

11. Drain the water through the buret tip into the sink.

12. Repeat Step 10 with two additional 10-mL volumes of distilled water.

III. Titrating the Fruit Juice

NOTE: If you have a standard NaOH solution from a previous experiment, such as **ANAL 426, Standardizing a Sodium Hydroxide Solution with a Standard Solution of Hydrochloric Acid**, use this solution for the following titration. If not, use the standard NaOH solution supplied by your laboratory instructor.

CAUTION

NaOH solution is corrosive and toxic, and it can cause skin burns. Prevent contact with your eyes, skin, and clothing. Do not ingest the solution.

If you spill any NaOH solution, immediately notify your laboratory instructor.

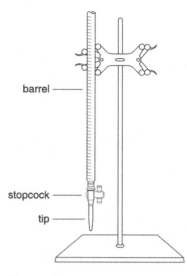

barrel

stopcock

tip

Figure 1
Titration apparatus

13. Obtain about 75 mL of standard NaOH solution in a clean, **dry** 125-mL Erlenmeyer flask. Stopper the flask with a new cork, and keep the flask stoppered when not in use. Record the exact molarity of the NaOH solution on your Data Sheet (4).

14. Rinse the buret with 5 mL of your standard NaOH solution. Hold the buret nearly horizontally. Rotate the buret so that the NaOH solution contacts the entire inner surface. Drain the solution through the buret tip into a 400-mL beaker labeled "Discarded Rinses and Titration Mixtures."

15. Repeat the buret rinsing with two additional 5-mL volumes of NaOH solution.

16. Clamp the buret to the support stand, as shown in Figure 1.

17. Place the labeled 400-mL beaker directly under the buret tip. Close the buret stopcock. Lower the buret until the tip extends about 3–4 cm into the beaker and rests against the inside wall.

18. Rinse the inner surface of your short-stem funnel twice, using 5 mL of NaOH solution each time. Collect the rinses in your discard beaker. Place the funnel in the open top of your buret.

NOTE: Make sure that the buret tip is filled with NaOH solution. There should not be any air bubbles in the solution between the stopcock and tip or in the solution in the buret barrel.

---

19. Close the stopcock. Fill the buret with NaOH solution to a level above the 0-mL calibration near the top of the buret. Remove the funnel from the buret, and place it in a clean 150-mL beaker.

20. Eliminate any air bubbles in the buret tip by carefully but rapidly rotating the stopcock a few times. Collect the small amount of drained NaOH solution in the "Discarded Rinses" beaker. Then, slowly drain NaOH solution into the beaker until the bottom of the meniscus is at, or slightly below, the 0-mL calibration.

21. Lift the beaker and touch the buret tip with the wet inner side wall of the beaker *above* the solution surface to remove the drop of NaOH solution that may be clinging to the tip.

NOTE: A 50-mL buret is calibrated in units of 0.1 mL, but measurements to the nearest 0.02 mL can be reproducibly estimated. Estimate the liquid level if it is between calibration marks, and record every reading to the nearest 0.02 mL.

When reading the meniscus in the buret, you may find it helpful to hold a white card marked with a dark stripe directly behind and with the stripe slightly below the meniscus, as shown in Figure 2 on the next page. Your line of sight must be level with the bottom of the meniscus.

---

22. Read the meniscus to the nearest 0.02 mL. Record this initial reading on your Data Sheet (6).

23. Place Erlenmeyer flask 1 under the buret tip. Lower the buret so that the tip extends about 3–4 cm into the mouth of the flask, as shown in Figure 3 on the next page.

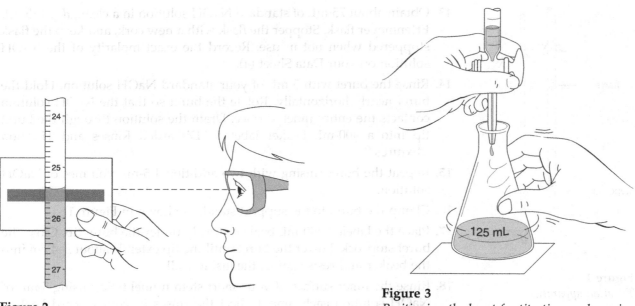

Figure 2
Reading a buret

Figure 3
*Positioning the buret for titration, and manip-
ulating the stopcock*

NOTE: If you are right-handed, gently swirl the flask with your right hand and control the stopcock with your left hand, as shown in Figure 3. If you are left-handed, swirl the flask with your left hand.

NOTE: As the titration proceeds, you will observe a pink coloration at the point where NaOH solution contacts the juice solution. As you approach the end point of the titration, the pink will begin to momentarily flash through the entire solution. At this point, begin adding the NaOH solution dropwise.

Because of the color of the fruit juice, the end point may be difficult to observe. Consult your laboratory instructor if you encounter difficulty detecting the end point.

---

24. Add 1- to 2-mL volumes of NaOH solution from theburet to the juice sample, while gently swirling the flask.

NOTE: Stop titrating when pink persists throughout the solution for 30 s after you have thoroughly swirled the flask. When this condition occurs, you have reached the end point.

---

25. Take a final buret reading after the titration is complete. Record this reading to the nearest 0.02 mL on your Data Sheet (5).

26. Refill the buret with your NaOH solution, following the procedure in Steps 19–21.

27. Titrate the juice sample in Erlenmeyer flask 2, using the procedure in Steps 22–25. Record your data under column 2 on your Data Sheet (3, 4, 5, 6).

28. Consult your laboratory instructor to determine whether or not you need to perform a third determination. If a third titration is necessary,

repeat Steps 3, 5, and 19–25, using a third juice sample. Record these titration data in the right margin of your Data Sheet.

After completing the third determination, ask your laboratory instructor to check and initial your Data Sheet (8).

29. Discard the NaOH solution remaining in your buret in the "Discarded Rinses and Titration Mixtures" beaker.

Thoroughly rinse your buret twice with 10 mL of tap water each time. Pour the rinses into the discard beaker. Then, rinse your buret twice with 10 mL of distilled water each time. Pour the rinses into the drain.

30. Empty the titration mixtures from Erlenmeyer flasks 1 and 2 into the "Discarded Rinses" beaker. Rinse each flask, following the procedure in Step 29.

31. Pour the remaining juice into the discard beaker. Rinse the juice beaker following the procedure in Step 29.

32. Unless your laboratory instructor indicates otherwise, pour any remaining standard NaOH solution into the discard beaker. Rinse the 125-mL flask, following the procedure in Step 29. Discard rinses into the discard beaker.

IV. Treating the "Discarded Rinses and Titration Mixtures" for Disposal

33. Add 2 drops of phenolphthalein indicator solution to the solution in the "Discarded Rinses and Titration Mixtures" beaker. Note the color of the solution in the beaker after adding the indicator. Record the color on your Data Sheet. (9)

NOTE: Your laboratory instructor will provide 1M HCl and 1M NaOH solutions prepared specifically for neutralizing "Discarded Rinses and Titration Mixtures." If these solutions are not dispensed from dropping bottles, your laboratory instructor will demonstrate and describe a satisfactory method for dispensing the solutions.

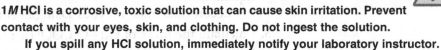

CAUTION

1M HCl is a corrosive, toxic solution that can cause skin irritation. Prevent contact with your eyes, skin, and clothing. Do not ingest the solution.

If you spill any HCl solution, immediately notify your laboratory instructor.

---

34. If the solution prepared in Step 33 is colorless, proceed to Step 35.

If the solution prepared in Step 33 is pink, add one drop of 1M HCl to the "Discarded Rinses and Titration Mixtures" beaker. Stir the solution with a glass stirring rod. Continue adding HCl solution dropwise, stirring after each addition, until the solution in the beaker *just* turns colorless.

Pour the colorless, neutralized solution into the drain, and dilute with a large amount of running water. Omit Step 35.

CAUTION

1M NaOH is corrosive and toxic, and it can cause skin burns. Prevent contact with your eyes, skin, and clothing. Do not ingest the solution.

If you spill any NaOH solution, immediately notify your laboratory instructor.

---

35. If the solution prepared in Step 33 is colorless, add one drop of $1M$ NaOH solution to the "Discarded Rinses and Titration Mixtures" beaker. Stir with a glass stirring rod. Continue adding NaOH solution dropwise, stirring after each addition, until the solution in the beaker *just* turns light pink.

Pour the light pink, neutralized solution into the drain, diluting with a large amount of running water. Rinse the beaker with tap water and with distilled water. Discard the rinses into the drain.

> ⚠ **CAUTION**
>
> **Wash your hands thoroughly with soap or detergent before leaving the laboratory.**

CALCULATIONS

Do the following calculations for each determination and record the results on your Data Sheet.

1. Find the volume, in milliliters, of NaOH solution used for the titration. To do so, subtract the initial buret reading (6) from the final buret reading (5).

    Record this volume on your Data Sheet (7).

2. Calculate the number of moles of NaOH required for the titration, using Equation 3.

    Record the number of moles on your Data Sheet (11).

3. Calculate the number of moles of $C_3H_5O(COOH)_3$ titrated, using Equation 4.

    Record the number of moles of $C_3H_5O(COOH)_3$ on your Data Sheet (12).

4. Calculate the mass of $C_3H_5O(COOH)_3$ present in the juice sample, using Equation 5.

    Record this mass on your Data Sheet (13).

5. Calculate the mass of $C_3H_5O(COOH)_3$ present in 1 mL of juice, using Equation 6.

    Record this mass on your Data Sheet (14).

6. Repeat these calculations, using the data from your second determination (7, 11–14).

7. Find the mean mass of $C_3H_5O(COOH)_3$ present in 1 mL of juice, using Equation 7.

$$\begin{array}{l} \text{mean mass of } C_3H_5O(COOH)_3 \\ \text{in 1 mL of juice, g} \end{array} = \frac{\begin{array}{c}\text{results from}\\\text{Calculation 5 for}\\\text{determination 1}\end{array} + \begin{array}{c}\text{results from}\\\text{Calculation 5 for}\\\text{determination 2}\end{array}}{2} \quad (Eq.\ 7)$$

Record the mean mass of $C_3H_5O(COOH)_3$ per 1 mL of juice on your Data Sheet (15).

_____   _____   _____
Name   *Section*   *Date*

Post-Laboratory Questions

(Use the spaces provided for the answers and additional paper if necessary.)

1. If available, compare your results with those of other class members who analyzed different juices. List the juices in order of increasing acidity.

type of juice	*g* $C_3H_5O(COOH)_3$ *mL*$^{-1}$
_____	_____
_____	_____
_____	_____
_____	_____

2. Briefly explain why it is essential that the flask in which you obtain the standard NaOH solution be completely dry, while the flask into which you pour the measured juice sample need not be dry.

3. A procedural change in this experiment would be required if a student wanted to determine the acidity of tomato juice by titrating a juice sample with NaOH solution. Briefly explain.

4. Briefly explain why you would probably obtain inaccurate results if you used the titration data you collected in this experiment to calculate the actual percent $C_3H_5O(COOH)_3$ in a juice sample.

_____   _____   _____
Name   *Section*   *Date*

Data Sheet

Experimental Data

I. Preparing the Fruit Juice for Titration

(1) type of fruit juice   _____

(2) code identification of fruit juice sample   _____

	determination	
	1	*2*
(3) volume of fruit juice transferred, mL	_____	_____

II. Titrating the Fruit Juice

	1	2
(4) molarity of NaOH solution, *M*	_____	_____
(5) final buret reading, mL	_____	_____
(6) initial buret reading, mL	_____	_____
(7) volume of NaOH used, mL	_____	_____

(8) acceptable titration results   _____

                                           laboratory instructor's initials

IV. Treating the "Discarded Rinses and Titration Mixtures" for Disposal

(9) color of "Discarded Rinses and Titration Mixtures" solution after addition   _____
of phenolphthalein indicator solution

(10) name and molarity of solution used to neutralize "Discarded Rinses and   _____
Titration Mixtures" solution

Treatment of Data

(11) number of moles of NaOH required, mol   _____

(12) number of moles of $C_3H_5O(COOH)_3$ titrated, mol   _____

(13) mass of $C_3H_5O(COOH)_3$ in sample, g   _____

(14) mass of $C_3H_5O(COOH)_3$ per mL of undiluted juice, g   _____

(15) mean mass of $C_3H_5O(COOH)_3$ per mL of undiluted juice, g   _____

_____   _____   _____
Name   _Section_   _Date_

Pre-Laboratory Assignment

1. Briefly explain why you should not drink any undiluted juice that has been brought into the laboratory.

2. Briefly explain the meaning of the following termsas they relate to this experiment.

   (1) titration

   (2) standard solution

   (3) indicator

3. Briefly describe the procedure you should follow if your fruit juice sample contains excess pulp.

4. A student followed the procedure in this experiment to determine the number of grams of $C_3H_5O(COOH)_3$ per 1 mL of an apple juice sample. The titration of 20.0 mL of the undiluted juice required 12.84 mL of $9.580 \times 10^{-2} M$ NaOH solution.

(1) Calculate the number of moles of NaOH required for the titration.

(2) Calculate the number of moles of $C_3H_5O(COOH)_3$ titrated.

(3) Calculate the mass of $C_3H_5O(COOH)_3$ present in the juice sample.

(4) Calculate the mass of $C_3H_5O(COOH)_3$ present in 1 mL of apple juice.

Heats of Neutralization
and Hess' Law

OBJECTIVE To determine the quantity of heat, ΔH, evolved in some acid-base reactions and to use these ΔH values to calculate ΔH for another reaction.

CONCEPT TO BE TESTED To show that the neutralization processes between strong acids and strong bases obey Hess' Law, since the net reaction is the same for all.

TEXT REFERENCES (1) Whitten, Davis, Peck, Stanley: 15.1 - 15.8 (2) Kotz, Treichel: 6.5 - 6.7 (3) Masterton, Hurley: 8.1 - 8.5 (4) Moore, Stanitski, Jurs: 6.3 - 6.9

LABORATORY MANUAL REFERENCES (1) Do not perform this experiment until you clearly understand how to handle any chemical or procedural hazards in a safe manner so that you prevent injury to yourself or others. Study Chemical Safety and Rules, pp 29-31. (2) The material covered in Background IX: Energy are basic to the understanding of this experiment.

INTRODUCTION

According to Hess' Law if several equations for chemical reactions can be manipulated and added together to give a single equation for another reaction, the value for the heat change of this last reaction is the sum of the heat changes for the reactions in which the equations were added to get this reaction equation. In this experiment you will use Hess' Law to calculate the ΔH for a fourth acid base reaction from the measured heat changes (ΔH) for three different acid-base reactions.

In your experiment, your calorimeter vessel will be two styrofoam cups, one nested inside the other, with a cardboard cover and thermometer (Figure 1).

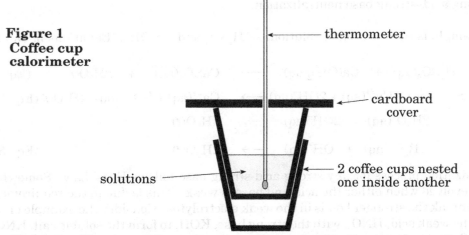

**Figure 1
Coffee cup
calorimeter**

thermometer

cardboard cover

2 coffee cups nested one inside another

solutions

Specific heat and heat capacity are two ways for expressing the energy associated with the temperature change in a substance. Specific Heat describes the amount of energy re-quired to change the temperature of a unit of mass of that substance by one degree. The units of energy most commonly used are the calorie and the joule (1 cal = 4.184 J).

$$\text{Specific Heat} = \frac{(\text{amount of heat, J})}{(\text{mass of substance})(\text{temperature change, }^\circ\text{C})}$$

$$\text{Specific Heat} = \frac{(\#\ \text{joules})}{(\#\ \text{grams})(\#\ ^\circ\text{C})} \qquad (\text{Eq. 1})$$

You will make a calculation of the heat capacity of your calorimeter plus thermometer. The equation defining the heat capacity is:

$$\text{Heat Capacity} = \frac{(\text{amount of heat, J})}{(\text{temperature change, °C})} \qquad \text{(Eq. 2)}$$

If one assumes that the specific heat of the dilute reaction solution is the same as the specific heat of the solvent water, measuring heat changes for reactions in dilute solution becomes simpler. You will use the calculations of the energy change of your calorimeter and of the dilute reaction solution to calculate the heats of reaction .

Hess' Law states that the change in the heat content, $\Delta H°_r$, for a given chemical or physical process depends only on the conditions in the initial and final states, and is the same regardless of the pathway by which the process takes place.

$$\Delta H°_r = \sum n\,\Delta H°_f(\text{products}) - \sum m\,\Delta H°_f(\text{reactants}) \qquad \text{(Eq. 3)}$$

The coefficients m and n are the number of moles of each reactant and each product.

Neutralization reactions of acids and bases are examples of reactions in solution. Common acid-base reactions involve the reaction of equal numbers of equivalents of the acid and the base to form a salt and water. The reaction of perchloric acid ($HClO_4$) and potassium hydroxide (KOH) to form the salt, potassium perchlorate ($KClO_4$) and water (Eq. 4) is an example. The total ionic equation (Eq. 4a) and the net ionic change (Eq. 4b) are given below. H^+ ions in water are shown as H_3O^+.

$$HClO_4(aq) + KOH(aq) \longrightarrow KClO_4(aq) + H_2O(\ell) \qquad \text{(Eq. 4)}$$

$$H_3O^+(aq) + ClO_4^-(aq) + K^+(aq) + OH^-(aq) \longrightarrow K^+(aq) + ClO_4^-(aq) + 2H_2O(\ell) \qquad \text{(Eq. 4a)}$$

$$H_3O^+(aq) + OH^-(aq) \longrightarrow 2H_2O(\ell) \qquad \text{(Eq. 4b)}$$

The net ionic equation (Eq. 1b) for strong acid, $HClO_4$, and strong base, KOH, is the same for any strong acid–strong base neutralization.

Another example is the reaction of solutions of H_2SO_4 and $Ca(OH)_2$ (Equations 5, 5a and 5b).

$$H_2SO_4(aq) + Ca(OH)_2(aq) \longrightarrow CaSO_4(aq) + 2H_2O(\ell) \qquad \text{(Eq. 5)}$$

$$2H_3O^+(aq) + SO_4^{2-}(aq) + Ca^{2+}(aq) + 2OH^-(aq) \longrightarrow Ca^{2+}(aq) + SO_4^{2-}(aq) + 4H_2O(\ell) \qquad \text{(Eq. 5a)}$$

$$2H_3O^+(aq) + 2OH^-(aq) \longrightarrow 4H_2O(\ell)$$

$$H_3O^+(aq) + OH^-(aq) \longrightarrow 2H_2O(\ell) \qquad \text{(Eq. 5b)}$$

The neutralization process for any strong acid-strong base follows Hess' Law. Somewhat less heat is evolved when either the acid and base is weak. This is due to the requirement of energy to break the stronger bonds in the weak electrolytes. Consider the example of the reaction of the weak acid, HNO_2, with the strong base, KOH, to form the soluble salt, KNO_2, and water (Equation 6).

$$HNO_2(aq) + KOH(aq) \longrightarrow KNO_2(aq) + H_2O(\ell) \qquad \text{(Eq. 6)}$$

$$HNO_2(aq) + K^+(aq) + OH^-(aq) \longrightarrow K^+(aq) + NO_2^-(aq) + H_2O(\ell) \qquad \text{(Eq. 6a)}$$

$$HNO_2(aq) + OH^-(aq) \longrightarrow NO_2^-(aq) + H_2O(\ell) \qquad \text{(Eq. 6b)}$$

Some of the heat evolved in the neutralization is consumed in the ionization of HNO_2. In this experiment you will measure the heat of reaction per mole for several acid-base reactions, both strong and weak, using the coffee-cup calorimeter. ΔH_r will be called ΔH_7, ΔH_8, ΔH_9, and ΔH_{10} in reference to Equations 7, 8, 9, and 10.

$$HCl(aq) + NaOH(aq) \longrightarrow NaCl(aq) + H_2O(\ell) \qquad \Delta H_7 = ? \quad (Eq. 7)$$

$$CH_3COOH(aq) + NaOH(aq) \longrightarrow NaCH_3COO(aq) + H_2O(\ell) \qquad \Delta H_8 = ? \quad (Eq. 8)$$

$$CH_3COOH(aq) + NH_3(aq) \longrightarrow NH_4CH_3COO(aq) \qquad \Delta H_9 = ? \quad (Eq. 9)$$

According to Hess' Law if several equations can be manipulated to give another equation such as [Eq. 7 – Eq. 8 + Eq 9)] = Eq. 10, then the sum of the ΔH's of the manipulated equations will be equal to the value of ΔH_{10}.

$$HCl(aq) + NH_3(aq) \longrightarrow NH_4Cl(aq) \qquad \Delta H_{10} = ? \quad (Eq. 10)$$

In this experiment you will calculate ΔH_{10} from ΔH_f (energies of formation) using a table of ΔH_f values in a reference text and Eq. 3. You will compare your experimentally determined ΔH_{10} value for Eq. 10 with the calculated value.

Example 1: Suppose you mixed 50.0 mL of 1.00 M solution of an acid, HA, with 50.0 mL of 1.00 M solution of a base, BOH, in a calorimeter (Figure 1) that has a Heat Capacity of 27 $^J/_{°C}$. Both solutions were initially at 21.7 °C. The temperature rises to 27.8 °C. Calculate ΔH_r.

Solution:

(a)   *Calculate the amount of heat absorbed by the solution. Assume the specific heat of the solution is the same as H_2O, 4.18 $^J/_{°C··g}$, and that its density is the same as H_2O, 1.00 g / mL.*

amt. of heat = sp. heat x mass x temp. change

no. J. absorbed = 4.18 $^J/_{g °C}$ x (50 g + 50 g) x (27.8 – 21.7) °C

= 2550 J

(b)   *Calculate amount of heat released in reaction*

| no. joules released | = | no. joules absorbed | + | no. joules absorbed |
| in reaction | | by solution | | by calorimeter |

= 2550 J   + [(27.8 – 21.7) °C x 27 $^J/_{°C}$]

= 2550 J   + 165 J

= 2715 J   =   2.7 x 10³ J

(c)   *Calculate the number of moles that reacted.*

$$\text{Number of moles of HA} = 50 \text{ mL} \times \frac{1 \text{ L}}{1000 \text{ mL}} \times \frac{1 \text{ mol HA}}{1 \text{ L}} = 0.050 \text{ mol HA}$$

$$\text{Number of moles of BOH} = 50 \text{ mL} \times \frac{1 \text{ L}}{1000 \text{ mL}} \times \frac{1 \text{ mol HA}}{1 \text{ L}} = 0.050 \text{ mol BOH}$$

(d)   *Calculate the Heat of Reaction per mole of H^+ that reacted. (1 mole of HA reacts with 1 mole BOH.*

$$0.050 \text{ mol HA} = 0.050 \text{ mol } H^+ = 2.7 \times 10^3 \text{ J}$$

$$\Delta H_r = \frac{2.7 \times 10^3 \text{ J}}{0.050 \text{ mol } H^+} = 5.4 \times 10^4 \frac{J}{\text{mol } H^+} = 54 \frac{kJ}{\text{mol } H^+}$$

**CAUTION! YOU MUST WEAR DEPARTMENTALLY APPROVED EYE PRO-
TECTION AT ALL TIMES YOU ARE IN THE LABORATORY!! KEEP ALL
REACTION VESSELS WELL AWAY FROM YOUR FACE!!**

PROCEDURE

(You may work in pairs if your Lab Instructor approves.) You will need a watch with a second hand or a stopwatch for the experiment.

A.   Calibration of thermometers

Step 1.   Obtain two 110 °C thermometers and label them "#1" and "#2."

Step 2.   Immerse both thermometers for two minutes in 150 mL of water contained in a 250 mL beaker.

Step 3.   Carefully read the temperature on each thermometer to the nearest 0.1 °C. Record these values on the REPORT FORM (3). (NOTE: The difference in these two values will be used as a correction factor to correct readings of #2 to the equivalent readings for #1. **Thermometer #1 will always be used in the calorimeter!**)

B.   Heat Capacity of Calorimeter

Step 4.   Assemble the calorimeter as shown in Figure 1. Use two 6-oz. styrofoam cups. The cardboard or styrofoam lid should have a hole just large enough to allow the insertion of the thermometer. Use a 1/4 inch section of rubber tubing around the thermometer to keep the bulb of the thermometer about 1/2 inch above the bottom of the cup.

Step 5.   Measure **50.0 mL of water** in a graduated cylinder and pour this into the *dry* calorimeter. Put the thermometer and lid in place and allow 5-10 minutes for the system to reach equilibrium.

Step 6.   Measure **50.0 mL of water** in a graduated cylinder and pour it into a *dry* 250 mL beaker.

Step 7.   Heat the water in the beaker to give a 10-15 °C temperature rise on thermometer #2. Let this sample stand for about 2 minutes to stabilize in temperature.

Step 8.   Record the temperature of the calorimeter and cool water (from Step 5) to the nearest 0.1 °C on the REPORT FORM (8). (NOTE: Since you will be making measurements over a period of time, the following four steps, 9-12, must be done as a quick series. First read all four steps and plan your actions.)

Step 9.   Record the temperature of the warm water in the beaker to the nearest 0.1 °C on the REPORT FORM (9).

Step 10.   (NOTE: Use a watch to time the readings. One student should make readings while the other keeps time and records the data.)

Step 11.   Remove the lid of the calorimeter and quickly add the warm water without splashing, and replace the lid. Begin recording the time measurements as soon as the warm water is added. Gently swirl the cups to mix the liquids. (NOTE: Do not break the thermometer.)

Step 12.   Record the temperature of the water every 10 seconds on the time-temperature data sheet until a maximum has been reached. Continue recording temperature readings every 30 seconds for 3 minutes. Record the data on **page 370** of the REPORT FORM (Step 12).

Step 13.   Plot the data (use a pencil) on a small portion of graph paper on **page 371** of the REPORT FORM as shown in Figure 2 and determine what the temperature should have been at time = zero seconds. Record this temperature on the REPORT FORM (13). (NOTE: Since you will be measuring the temperature change for four reactions, this type plot will be done for each reaction. You can see that the calorimeter is losing heat to the surroundings!)

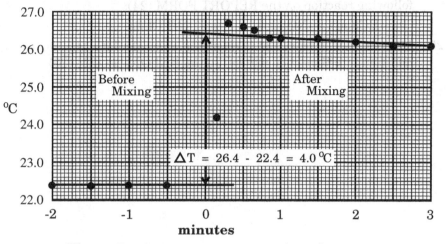

Figure 2. A temperature versus time plot.

Step 14.   Calculate the heat capacity of *your* calorimeter from your data and record this value on the REPORT FORM (14a, b, c, d).

C.   *Heats of Neutralization of Acids and Bases*

Step 15.   Rinse and dry the calorimeter.

Step 16.   Measure **50.0 mL of the standardized HCl (3.00 ±0.10 *M*)** in a *dry* graduated cylinder and pour it into the calorimeter. Calculate the number of moles of acid in this volume. Record the exact concentration and number of moles of acid on the REPORT FORM (16). Replace the lid and thermometer #1.

Step 17.   Measure **50.0 mL of the standardized NaOH (3.00 ±0.10 *M*)** in a *dry* graduated cylinder. Calculate the number of moles of base in this volume. Record the exact concentration and number of moles of base on the REPORT FORM (17).

Step 18.   Adjust the temperature of the base to the same temperature as the acid in the calorimeter. (NOTE: You may use warmth of your hands or cool running water for this adjustment.) Record this temperature as the initial temperature, T_i, on the REPORT FORM (18).)

NOTE: Steps 19-20 must be performed quickly. Read all the steps and plan your actions!

Step 19.   Remove the lid from the calorimeter, pour in the base solution without splashing, and replace the lid and thermometer. Begin stirring and measuring temperature time.

Step 20.   Use the procedure in steps 11, 12, and 13 to determine the temperature at time = zero seconds on the REPORT FORM (20).

Step 21.   Determine the change in temperature, ΔT, and record the value on the REPORT FORM (21a). Calculate the total heat evolved for this quantity of reactants (21b). (NOTE: Use Example 20.2 as a guide.)

Step 22.   Calculate the ΔH_7 per mole of acid neutralized on the REPORT FORM (22).

Step 23.   Repeat Steps 15-22 for each of these acid-base pairs (a) $CH_3COOH/NaOH$, and (b) CH_3COOH/NH_3. Calculate ΔH_8 and ΔH_9 per mole of acid neutralized in Equations 5 and 6 and record your data and results on the REPORT FORM (16-22).

Step 24.   Use your value for the ΔH_7, ΔH_8 and ΔH_9 and Hess' Law to calculate ΔH_{10} for the following reaction on the REPORT FORM (24):

$$HCl(aq) + NH_3(aq) \longrightarrow NH_4Cl(aq)$$

Step 25.   Use ΔH_f values from a text reference and calculate ΔH_{10} for the same reaction and compare these two values on the REPORT FORM (25).

Name _____   Lab Instructor _____

Date _____   Lab Section _____

Prelab Questions

1. Define the following terms and describe how they relate to this experiment.
    a. ΔH°_r

    b. specific heat

    c. calorimeter

    d. endothermic

2. What is the significance of the point 24.4°C on the plot like Figure 2?

3. Consider the reaction of 50.0 mL of 1.12 M $HC_2H_3O_2$ with 50.0 mL of 1.27 M NH_3.
    (a)   How many moles of $HC_2H_3O_2$ and of NH_3 are initially present?

(b)   How many moles of $HC_2H_3O_2$ and of NH_3 are actually neutralized?

4.   The complete neutralization of 0.0527 moles of a monoprotic acid with excess NaOH evolves 2.82 kJ of heat. What is the molar heat of neutralization of the acid with NaOH from this data.

5.   A student collected the following data while determining the molar heat of neutralization of a monoprotic acid, HA, with NaOH. Calculate the molar heat of neutralization of this acid with NaOH. Assume that the specific heats of the solutions are the same as water.

a) temperature of HA and NaOH before mixing	23.7 °C
b) concentration of the acid, HA	1.06 M
c) concentration of the NaOH	1.12 M
d) volume of the acid, HA, used	50.0 mL
e) volume of the base, NaOH, used	50.0 mL
f) temperature of calorimeter and mixture at time = 0	29.7 °C
g) heat capacity of calorimeter	6.9 $^J/_{°C}$

REPORT FORM:

Name _____

Heats of Neutralization

Lab Instructor _____

Lab Section _____

Date _____

A. *Calibration of the Thermometers*

Step No.

3.   Temperature of thermometer #1   Temperature of thermometer #2

in tap water: _____ °C   in tap water: _____ °C

Correction factor applied to thermometer #2

to make readings equal thermometer #1:   _____ °C. (Indicate + or −)

B. *Heat Capacity of the Calorimeter (Calorimeter Constant)*
(Show your calculations with appropriate units.)

Step No.

8.   Temperature of calorimeter and cool H_2O _____ °C

9.   Temperature of warm H_2O _____ °C

13.   Temperature of the mixture at time = 0
determined from the Temp/Time plot   _____ °C

14a. Amount of heat released by warm water   _____ J

b.   Amount of heat absorbed by cool water   _____ J

c.   Amount of heat absorbed by calorimeter   _____ J

d.   Heat capacity of calorimeter   _____ $^{J}/_{°C}$

C. Heat of Neutralization of Acids and Bases

(1)   Show each step in your calculations for ΔH_4.

$$HCl(aq) + NaOH(aq) \longrightarrow NaCl(aq) + H_2O(\ell) \qquad \text{(Eq. 7)}$$

Step No.

16.   50.0 mL _____ M HCl   Number of moles of HCl _____ mol

17.   50.0 mL _____ M NaOH   Number of moles of NaOH _____ mol

         Which reagent is the limiting reagent   _____

         What is the number of moles of HCl neutralized   _____ mol

18.   Temperature of the reactants before mixing   _____ °C

20.   Temperature of the reaction mixture at Time = 0 sec

            determined from the Temp/Time plot.   _____ °C

21.   Temperature change for the reaction   _____ °C

22.   Amount of heat absorbed by the solution   _____ J

         Amount of heat absorbed by the calorimeter   _____ J

         Total amount of heat evolved by neutralization reaction   _____ J

         Amount of heat evolved per mole of HCl neutralized, ΔH_4 _____ J

         Balanced molecular equation

         Balanced net ionic equation

REPORT FORM:

Heats of Neutralization

Name _____

Lab Instructor _____

Lab Section _____

Date _____

(3) Show each step in your calculations for ΔH_5.

$$CH_3COOH(aq) + NaOH(aq) \longrightarrow NaCH_3COO(aq) + H_2O(\ell) \qquad (Eq. \ 8)$$

Repeat Step No.

16. 50.0 mL _____ M CH_3COOH Number of moles of CH_3COOH _____ mol

17. 50.0 mL _____ M NaOH Number of moles of NaOH _____ mol

Which reagent is the limiting reagent

What is the number of moles of CH_3COOH neutralized _____ mol

18. Temperature of the reactants before mixing _____ °C

20. Temperature of the reaction mixture at T= 0 sec _____ °C
    determined from the Temp/Time plot.

21. Temperature change for the reaction _____ °C

22. Amount of heat absorbed by the solution _____ J

Amount of heat absorbed by the calorimeter _____ J

Total amount of heat evolved by neutralization reaction _____ J

Amount of heat evolved per mole of CH_3COOH neutralized, ΔH_5 _____ J

Balanced molecular equation

Balanced net ionic equation

(4) Show each step in your calculations for ΔH_6.

$$CH_3COOH(aq) + NH_3(aq) \longrightarrow NH_4CH_3COO(aq) \qquad \text{(Eq. 9)}$$

Repeat Step No.

16.   50.0 mL _____ M CH$_3$COOH   Number of moles of CH$_3$COOH _____ mol

17.   50.0 mL _____ MNH$_3$ Number of moles of NH$_3$ _____ mol

Which reagent is the limiting reagent   _____

What is the number of moles of HCl neutralized   _____ mol

18.   Temperature of the reactants before mixing   _____ °C

20.   Temperature of the reaction mixture at T=0 sec   _____ °C
       determined from the Temp/Time plot.

21.   Temperature change for the reaction   _____ °C

22.   Amount of heat absorbed by the solution   _____ J

Amount of heat absorbed by the calorimeter   _____ J

Total amount of heat evolved by neutralization reaction   _____ J

Amount of heat evolved per mole of CH$_3$COOH neutralized, ΔH_6 _____ J

Balanced molecular equation

Balanced net ionic equation

REPORT FORM:

Heats of Neutralization

Name _____

Lab Instructor _____

Lab Section _____

Date _____

Step 24. Hess' Law

<u>ΔH neutralization</u>

$HCl(aq) + NaOH(aq) \longrightarrow NaCl(aq) + H_2O$ $\Delta H_7 =$ _____ kJ/mol

$CH_3COOH(aq) + NaOH(aq) \longrightarrow CH_3COONa(aq) + H_2O$ $\Delta H_8 =$ _____ kJ/mol

$CH_3COOH(aq) + NH_3(aq) \longrightarrow CH_3COONH_4(aq)$ $\Delta H_9 =$ _____ kJ/mol

Write these equations as total ionic equations and manipulate them and their enthalpy changes to calculate the enthalpy change for the reaction given below (ΔH_7).

<u>Reaction</u>

<u>ΔH</u>

_____   _____ kJ/mol

_____   _____ kJ/mol

_____   _____ kJ/mol

$HCl(aq) + NH_3(aq) \longrightarrow NH_4Cl(aq)$ $\Delta H_{10} =$ _____ kJ/mol
(from *experimental* data)

Step 25.

$$\Delta H^{\circ}_{10} = \{\Delta H^{\circ}_f [NH_4Cl(aq)]\} - \{\Delta H^{\circ}_f [HCl(aq)] + \Delta H^{\circ}_f [NH_3(aq)]\}$$

Handbook values: $\Delta H^{\circ}_f [NH_4Cl(aq)]$ = _____ kJ/mol

$\Delta H^{\circ}_f [HCl(aq)]$ = _____ kJ/mol

$\Delta H^{\circ}_f [NH_3(aq)]$ = _____ kJ/mol

Calculation of ΔH°_{10} from *handbook* values:

TIME-TEMPERATURE DATA
Mixed Solutions

Time Sec	Water Water	Sec	HCl NaOH	Sec	CH₃COOH NaOH	Sec	CH₃COOH NH₃
Step 12		Step 20		Step 23		Step 23'	

REPORT FORM: Name _____

Heats of Neutralization

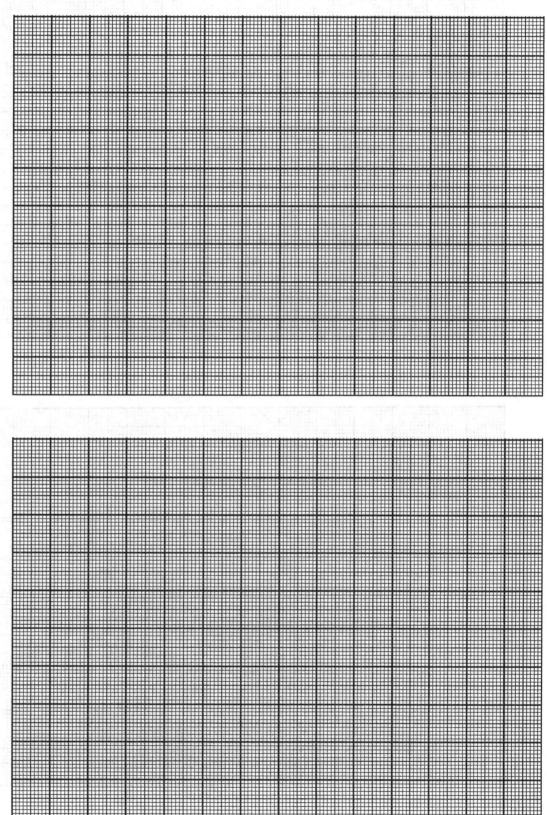

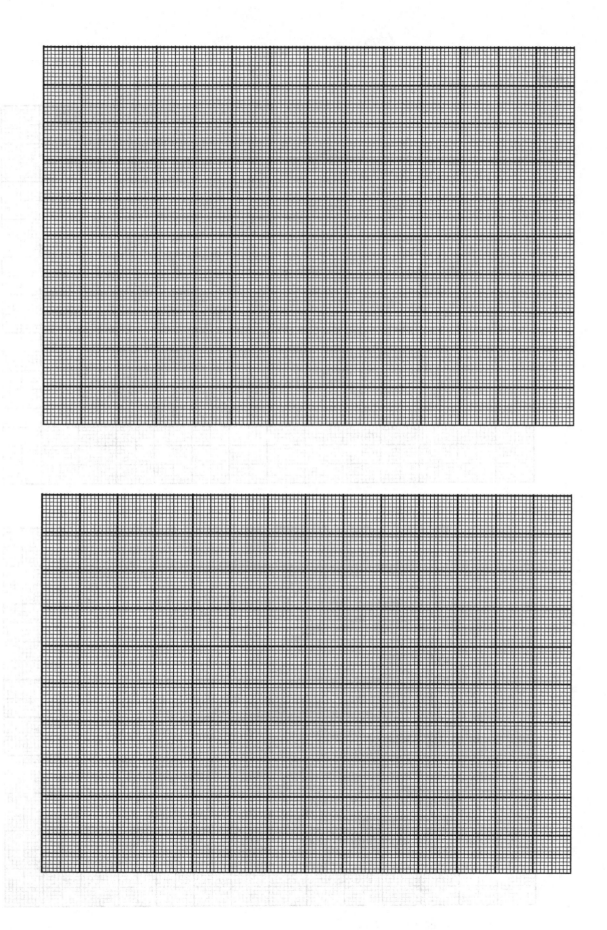

Name _____   Lab Instructor _____

Date _____   Lab Section _____

Post-Lab Questions

1.   Consider these possible sources of error described below. Briefly explain the effect of each on your calculated molar heats of neutralization. Indicate which item(s) of data would be in error and the effect (too large, too small or no effect).

   (a) Step 15: The calorimeter cup had several milliliters of water in it when you added the HCl in Step 16.

   (b) Step 19: The base solution was added to the acid solution but was not stirred while temperature measurements were made.

   (c) Step 11: Some of the base splashed out of the calorimeter while pouring.

2..   Following the procedure described in Steps 4-13 of this experiment, this data was obtained when a glass calorimeter was calibrated. Calculate the heat capacity (calorimeter constant) for this calorimeter in $^{J}/_{°C}$.
   a)   Temperature of the calorimeter and 50.0 mL of cool water   20.4 °C
   b)   Temperature of 50 mL warm water   39.5 °C
   c)   Temperature of the calorimeter and mixture at time = 0   28.1 °C

3. (a) What reactions besides neutralization takes place with acetic acid and NH_3 to make the heat of neutralization different than for HCl/NaOH?

    (b) Which of these acids, CH_3COOH or HCl, should have the lesser exothermic heat of neutralization?

Spectrophotometric Analysis of Permanganate Ion Solutions

Prepared by Donald F. Clemens and Warren A. McAllister, East Carolina University

PURPOSE OF THE EXPERIMENT

Spectrophotometrically analyze permanganate ion solutions of unknown concentration.

BACKGROUND INFORMATION

The characteristics of colored solutions have been of interest to chemists for a long time. Of particular interest has been the fact that colored solutions, when irradiated with white light, will selectively absorb incident light of some wavelengths but not of others. We can determine the particular wavelength or group of wavelengths absorbed by systematically exposing the solution to monochromatic light of different wavelengths and recording the responses. If light of a particular wavelength is not absorbed, the intensity of the beam directed at the solution (I_o) will match the intensity of the beam transmitted by the solution (I_t). If some of the light is absorbed, the intensity of the beam transmitted by the solution will be less than that of the incoming beam. The ratio of I_t to I_o can be used to indicate the percent of the incoming light that is absorbed by the solution, as shown in Equation 1. The wavelength at which **percent transmittance (%T)** is lowest is the wavelength to which the solution is most sensitive. This wavelength, which is used for analysis, is the **analytical wavelength.**

$$\%T = \left(\frac{I_t}{I_o}\right)(100\%) \qquad \text{(Eq. 1)}$$

Once we determine the analytical wavelength for a particular solution, we can study the three variables that influence the specific response of the solution. These variables are the **concentration (c)** of the absorbing substance in the solution, the **pathlength (b)** of the light through the solution, and the sensitivity of the absorbing species to the energy of the analytical wavelength. When concentration is expressed in molarity (mol L^{-1}), and the pathlength is measured in centimeters (cm), the sensitivity factor is known as the **molar absorptivity (ε)** of the particular absorbing species. Molar absorptivity is a proportionality constant of a particular absorbing species with units of L mol^{-1} cm^{-1}. Its value depends on the analytical wavelength used for the analysis. The product of these three variables is **absorbance (A)**, as shown in Equation 2.

$$A = \varepsilon bc \qquad \text{(Eq. 2)}$$

This relationship is known as **Beer's law**. We can also define absorbance in terms of I_o and I_t, as given in Equation 3.

$$A = \log \left(\frac{I_o}{I_t} \right) \qquad \text{(Eq. 3)}$$

A **spectrophotometer** is an instrument used to study the response of solutions to light. It has two scales, one calibrated to display percent transmittances and the other calibrated to display absorbances. The absorbance scale is logarithmic with values ranging from zero to infinity. The percent transmittance scale is linear with values ranging from zero to 100. It is easier to read the linear scale accurately, because the distance between units is constant. Readings on the percent transmittance scale can be converted to equivalent absorbances, using Equation 4.

$$A = 2.000 - \log(\%T) \qquad \text{(Eq. 4)}$$

We can see from Equation 2 that the absorbance of a solution is directly proportional to the concentration of the absorbing substance in solution. Often several components of a solution absorb energy of the wavelength being used for the analysis. To compensate for this interference we prepare a **reference solution**, or **blank**, that contains all the components of the solution, except the species being determined. The spectrophotometer is set so that 100% of the light of the chosen wavelength is transmitted by the reference solution. Thus, any absorbance by a solution will be due to the presence of the substance being studied.

If sample containers, called **cuvettes**, of uniform size are used, the absorbance of a series of solutions will, according to Beer's law, be proportional to the concentration of the absorbing substance in the solutions. The linear relationship between concentration and absorbance shown in Figure 1 is typical of many chemical systems that are said to follow Beer's law. This plot of absorbance versus concentration is referred to as a **Beer's law plot**.

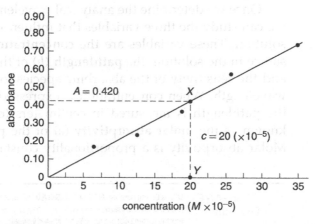

Figure 1
A typical Beer's law plot

Note, however, such systems cannot be shown to follow Beer's law throughout the range of all possible concentrations. This is true for a variety of reasons, one being the limitations of the spectrophotometer. The sensitivity of most spectrophotometers is greatest between 10 and 90 %T. Using only percent transmittances falling in the most sensitive meter range, and Equation 4, we can correctly determine equivalent absorbances.

For instance, for $\%T = 10\%$,

$$A = 2.000 - \log 10 = 2.000 - 1.000 = 1.000$$

and for $\%T = 90\%$,

$$A = 2.000 - \log 90 = 2.000 - 1.954 = 0.046$$

Of course, the effective concentration range for a particular absorbing substance will depend on the magnitude of the molar absorptivity of the substance at the analytical wavelength. If we know, or can determine, this value, then we can determine a concentration range over which we would expect to obtain a linear relationship between concentration and absorbance.

A variety of chemical factors can cause deviations from the expected linear relationship between concentration and absorbance. One common problem occurs when the absorbing substances are particularly sensitive to hydrogen ion concentration. If the pH of a series of solutions of one substance is kept constant, but the concentration of the absorbing substance is changed, then the equilibrium-favoring formation of the absorbing substance may shift unexpectedly. The chromate–dichromate equilibrium shown in Equation 5 is a well-known example of a chemical system that responds in this way.

$$2\,CrO_4{}^{2-}(aq) + 2\,H_3O^+(aq) \rightleftharpoons Cr_2O_7{}^{2-}(aq) + 3\,H_2O(\ell) \qquad \text{(Eq. 5)}$$

The relationship between absorbance and concentration is used extensively in quantitative analysis. In one application, a series of solutions of known concentrations of a substance is prepared. The percent transmittance of each is read at the analytical wavelength. After converting the percent transmittances to equivalent absorbances, a Beer's law plot can be made. If the absorbance of a solution of unknown concentration of the same substance is then measured, the concentration can be read directly from the plot. Figure 1 shows how this would be done for a solution with a calculated absorbance of 0.420.

The instrument most widely used for this type of analysis is a spectrophotometer. Figure 2 on the next page shows the arrangement of the optics in a spectrophotometer such as the Spectronic 20. The light generated by the tungsten lamp passes through the entrance slit and is reflected by the diffraction grating. The grating acts like a prism, separating the white light into monochromatic beams of various wavelengths. A desired wavelength is selected by rotating a cam that allows the light to pass through a narrow exit slit. Thus a nearly monochromatic beam of light is produced. The light that passes through the exit slit passes through the sample and finally strikes the measuring photoelectric cell or phototube. Here the light energy is converted to an electric signal.

In this experiment, you will prepare a potassium permanganate ($KMnO_4$) solution of known concentration and then determine the analytical

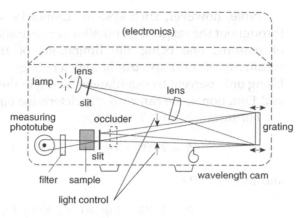

Figure 2
Optics of a spectrophotometer

wavelength for the solution. You will find this wavelength by measuring the percent transmittance at 20-nm increments over the range from 480 to 600 nm, converting percent transmittance to absorbance, and plotting absorbance versus wavelength.

Next, you will measure the percent transmittance of a series of $KMnO_4$ solutions of known concentrations at the analytical wavelength of a permanganate ion solution. After calculating the absorbance and the molarity of each solution, you will prepare a Beer's law plot by plotting absorbance against the molar concentration of the permanganate ion for each solution.

Finally, you will measure the percent transmittance of a permanganate ion solution of $KMnO_4$ of unknown concentration at the analytical wavelength. After calculating the absorbance, you will find the concentration of the unknown solution from your Beer's law plot.

PROCEDURE

CHEMICAL ALERT

dilute potassium permanganate solution—mild oxidant and irritant
3M sulfuric acid—corrosive and oxidant

CAUTION

Wear departmentally approved eye protection while doing this experiment.

I. Operating a Spectrophotometer

If the instrument you are using for this experiment is not a Spectronic 20, your laboratory instructor will give you directions for using the specific instrument available.

Turning on the power to the instrument

Rotate the left-hand knob, the **amplifier control**, clockwise. On some models, a red LED will light at this point. Allow about 15 min for the instrument to warm up before recording any measurements.

Cleaning cuvettes

While waiting for the instrument to warm up, rinse two cuvettes with distilled or deionized water. Then, rinse one of the cuvettes three times with the solution to be measured. Fill this cuvette three-quarters full with the solution to be measured. Fill the other cuvette three-quarters full with distilled water or the solution you are using as the reference solution. Do not handle the lower portion of the cuvettes, because smudges or droplets of solution will affect the passage of the light beam through the cuvette. Wipe off the outside of the cuvettes with an absorbent tissue before inserting the cuvette in the clamp holder.

Setting the wavelength

Turn the **wavelength control knob**, on the top of the instrument, until the appropriate wavelength setting appears on the scale visible at the left of the knob. Do not change the setting during the experiment unless specifically instructed to do so.

Setting 0% transmittance

Make the following adjustment with no cuvette in the sample holder; under this condition, no light strikes the phototube. About 15 min after turning the instrument on, adjust the left-hand knob, the amplifier control, so that the needle on the meter points to zero on the percent transmittance scale.

Setting 100% transmittance

Turn the right-hand knob, the **light control**, counterclockwise almost to its limit before inserting a cuvette into the sample holder. Insert the cuvette containing the reference solution into the sample holder. Match exactly the index line on the cuvette with the index line on the holder. Close the top of the holder tightly. Turn the right-hand knob clockwise until the needle points to 100 on the percent transmission scale. Immediately remove the test tube to avoid fatiguing the phototube, and proceed to the sample measurement.

Check 0 and 100% transmittance

After the cuvette is removed from the sample holder, an occluder automatically drops into the light beam path. The needle should then point to zero. Each time the wavelength is changed, and during any extensive series of measurements at the same wavelength, the 0 and 100% transmittance settings should be checked. If necessary, reset these two settings using the procedure described above.

II. Determining the Analytical Wavelength

CAUTION

Sulfuric acid is a corrosive, toxic substance that can cause severe skin burns. Prevent eye, skin, and clothing contact. Clean up any spillage following the directions of your laboratory instructor.

Add approximately 125 mL of distilled water to a clean 250-mL volumetric flask. Measure 10 mL of 3.0M sulfuric acid (H_2SO_4) with a clean, dry graduated cylinder. Carefully add the acid to the water in the volumetric flask.

CAUTION

Potassium permanganate solution is an oxidant and a skin irritant that can cause discoloration of the skin. Prevent eye, skin, and clothing contact. Clean up any spillage following the directions of your laboratory instructor.

CAUTION

Never use your mouth to draw a solution into a pipet. Always use a rubber bulb to fill a pipet.

Rinse a clean, 10-mL pipet with about 2 mL of a $4.00 \times 10^{-3} M$ KMnO$_4$ solution. Draw the solution into the pipet using a rubber bulb. Quickly disconnect the rubber bulb and place your index finger over the top opening to prevent the water from draining out of it. Hold the pipet in a nearly horizontal position. Rotate the pipet so that the rinse solution contacts as much of the inner surface of the pipet as possible. Remove your finger briefly during this process to allow the solution to enter the upper stem of the pipet. Drain the solution through the tip of the pipet into a beaker.

NOTE: After you discharge a solution from a pipet, there will be a small amount of liquid left in the tip of the pipet. Do not blow this liquid out of the pipet. The pipet is calibrated to deliver 10.00 mL of solution **excluding** the small amount remaining in the tip of the pipet.

Repeat the rinsing procedure with two additional portions of the solution. Discard the rinse solutions, following the directions of your laboratory instructor.

Pipet 10.00 mL of $4.0 \times 10^{-3} M$ KMnO$_4$ into the acid in the volumetric flask. As you release the solution into the flask, hold the tip of the pipet against the side of the flask. Allow the solution to flow down the side of the flask to avoid splattering. After you deliver the solution from the pipet, continue to hold the tip of the pipet against the side of the flask for an additional 15 s.

Add distilled water to the solution in the flask until the bottom of the meniscus of the solution is at the base of the flask neck. Stopper the flask. While firmly holding the stopper with your forefinger, invert the flask 10 times to thoroughly mix the solution.

After the trapped air bubbles rise to the surface, add distilled water until the bottom of the meniscus coincides with the calibration mark on the neck of the flask. Stopper the flask. While firmly holding the stopper with your forefinger, invert the flask 10 times to thorouqhly mix the solution. Label this flask Solution 1.

Set the instrument to 100% T using a cuvette three-quarters filled with distilled water, the reference solution.

Rinse another cuvette three times with the diluted KMnO$_4$ solution. Discard the rinse solution each time, following the directions of your laboratory instructor. Fill the cuvette three-quarters full with the solution. Be careful to avoid leaving fingerprints on the cuvette. Carefully wipe the outside of the cuvette with an absorbent tissue. Check to make certain that you have removed all fingerprints.

Insert the cuvette containing the $KMnO_4$ solution into the sample holder. Match exactly the index line on the cuvette with the line on the holder. Close the top of the holder tightly. Immediately read the percent transmittance to three significant digits, and record it on your Data Sheet.

Remove the cuvette from the sample holder. Change the wavelength to 500 nm. Reset the instrument at 0 and 100% transmittance, using the cuvette containing distilled water. Reinsert the cuvette containing the $KMnO_4$ solution into the sample holder. Read the percent transmittance to three significant digits, and record it on your Data Sheet.

Repeat this procedure using wavelengths of 520, 540, 560, 580, and 600 nm. Record all percent transmittance readings on your Data Sheet.

Under the section on Calculations, convert the transmittance to absorbance and prepare a graph by plotting absorbance versus wavelength. Select the analytical wavelength for permanganate ion solution from the graph. Use this wavelength for the other determinations in Sections III and IV of this experiment.

Discard the solution in the cuvette, following the directions of your laboratory instructor. Thoroughly rinse the cuvette with distilled water.

III. Preparing a Beer's Law Plot

Your laboratory instructor will assign you one or more of the solutions listed in Table 1.

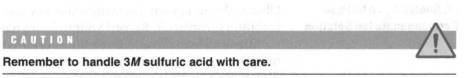

CAUTION

Remember to handle 3*M* sulfuric acid with care.

Add approximately 125 mL of distilled water to a clean 250-mL volumetric flask. Measure 10 mL of $3.0M$ H_2SO_4 with a clean, dry graduated cylinder. Carefully add the acid to the water in the volumetric flask. With a pipet and a rubber bulb, add the assigned volume of $4.00 \times 10^{-3}M$ $KMnO_4$ to the flask. Record the original molarity of the $KMnO_4$ solution and the volume of solution used on your Data Sheet.

Add distilled water to the solution in the flask until the bottom of the meniscus of the solution is at the base of the flask neck. Stopper the flask. While firmly holding the stopper with your forefinger, invert the flask 10 times to thoroughly mix the solution.

After the trapped air bubbles rise to the surface, add distilled water until the bottom of the meniscus coincides with the calibration mark on the neck of the flask. Stopper the flask. While firmly holding the stopper with

Table 1 *Laboratory assignments for preparing the Beer's law plot*

assignment number	volume of $4.00 \times 10^{-3}M$ $KMnO_4$, mL	solution number
1	10.0	2
2	8.0	3
3	6.0	4
4	4.0	5
5	2.0	6
6	1.0	7

your forefinger, invert the flask 10 times to thoroughly mix the solution. Label this flask according to your laboratory assignment.

Set the instrument at the analytical wavelength for the permanganate ion solution. Rezero the instrument, using distilled water as the reference solution. Read the percent transmittance of this permanganate ion solution following the procedure you used previously. Record the percent transmittance of your assigned solution to three significant digits on your Data Sheet.

Discard the solution in the cuvette, following the directions of your laboratory instructor. Thoroughly rinse the cuvette with distilled water.

Repeat the above procedure using other assigned solutions of potassium permanganate, as instructed. After measuring the percent transmittance of each solution, reset the instrument at 0 and 100% transmittance, using the reference solution, after measuring the percent transmittance of each solution.

Before leaving the laboratory, obtain from other members of your class or from your laboratory instructor the data for the other permanganate ion solutions used in this experiment. Record these data on your Data Sheet.

Complete the steps in Part III of the Calculations section of this module before analyzing your unknown.

IV. Analyzing an Unknown Permanganate Ion Solution

Obtain the unknown permanganate ion solution or solutions from your laboratory instructor. Record your unknown number(s) on your Data Sheet.

Rinse a clean cuvette three times each with a fresh portion of the first unknown solution. Discard the rinse solution each time, following the directions of your laboratory instructor. Fill the cuvette three-quarters full with the unknown solution.

Check to be sure the instrument is set at the analytical wavelength for the permanganate ion solution. Use the reference solution to reset the 0 and 100% transmittance settings, if necessary.

Insert the cuvette containing the unknown solution. Close the cover tightly. Measure the percent transmittance to three significant digits at the analytical wavelength. Record the percent transmittance on your Data Sheet.

Discard the solution in the cuvette, following the directions of your laboratory instructor. Thoroughly rinse the cuvette with distilled water.

After you have made all of your measurements with the spectrophotometer, follow the directions of your laboratory instructor for turning off the instrument.

CAUTION ⚠️

Wash your hands thoroughly with soap or detergent before leaving the laboratory.

CALCULATIONS

Do the following calculations and record the results on your Data Sheet.

II. Determining the Analytical Wavelength

1. From the percent transmittance readings, calculate the absorbance for each measurement made, using Equation 4.

2. Plot the absorbance on the ordinate and the wavelength on the abscissa for the readings within the range 480–600 nm. Connect the plotted points with a smooth curve, and determine the analytical wavelength for a permanganate ion solution.

III. Preparing a Beer's Law Plot

3. Calculate the molar concentration of each solution used.

$$\text{number of moles of } KMnO_4 \text{ used} = (\text{molarty, mol L}^{-1})(\text{inital volume, L})$$

$$\text{molarity of final solution of } KMnO_4, \ M = \frac{\text{number of moles of } KMnO_4}{\text{final volume of solution, L}}$$

4. Calculate the absorbance for each solution from the percent transmittance, using Equation 4.

5. Construct a Beer's law plot by plotting the absorbance on the ordinate and the molar concentration of the permanganate ion on the abscissa. Draw the best straight line through the plotted points. The extrapolated line should pass through the origin.

IV. Analyzing an Unknown Permanganate Ion Solution

6. Calculate the absorbance for your unknown solution from the percent transmittance, using Equation 4.

7. From the Beer's law plot prepared in Part III, find the molar concentration of your permanganate ion unknown solution.

_____   _____   _____
Name   *Section*   *Date*

Post-Laboratory Questions

(*Use the spaces provided for the answers and additional paper if necessary.*)

1. A student, following the procedure in this experiment, determined the percent transmittance of two solutions of unknown concentration. The first was 96% and the second was 3%.

    (1) Convert the first percent transmittance to an equivalent absorbance. Briefly explain why the student should or should not be confident in reading the concentration of permanganate ion in the unknown directly from the Beer's law plot.

    (2) Convert the second percent transmittance to an equivalent absorbance. Briefly explain why the student could not have read this percent transmittance accurately from the absorbance scale on the spectrophotometer.

    (3) Briefly explain why the student should or should not be confident in reading the concentration of the second unknown directly from the Beer's law plot.

(4) Suggest something the student could do with the second sample that would make the determination of the concentration of permanganate ion more accurate.

2. Bathophenanthroline is a compound that forms a red complex with iron(II). The molar absorptivity for the complex is 22,350 L mol^{-1} cm^{-1} at $\lambda = 535$ nm.

(1) Determine the molar concentration range of the iron(II)–bathophenanthroline complex that can be analyzed directly with a spectrophotometer, using a 1-cm cuvette.

(2) Convert the molar concentrations determined in (1) to grams of iron(II) per liter of solution. Comment on the sensitivity of the method in determining iron(II).

_____   _____   _____
Name   *Section*   *Date*

Data Sheet 1

II. Determining the Analytical Wavelength

wavelength, nm	*%T*	*absorbance, A*
480	_____	_____
500	_____	_____
520	_____	_____
540	_____	_____
560	_____	_____
580	_____	_____
600	_____	_____

analytical wavelength, nm   _____

%T at analytical wavelength   _____

III. Preparing a Beer's Law Plot

original molarity of $KMnO_4$ solution, M _____

volume of $KMnO_4$ stock solution used, mL   _____

final volume of solution, after dilution, mL   _____

solution	*%T*	*absorbance, A*	*molarity, M*
2	_____	_____	_____
3	_____	_____	_____
4	_____	_____	_____
5	_____	_____	_____
6	_____	_____	_____
7	_____	_____	_____

IV. Analyzing an Unknown Permanganate Ion Solution

code number of unknown	*%T*	*absorbance, A*	*molarity, M*
_____	_____	_____	_____
_____	_____	_____	_____
_____	_____	_____	_____

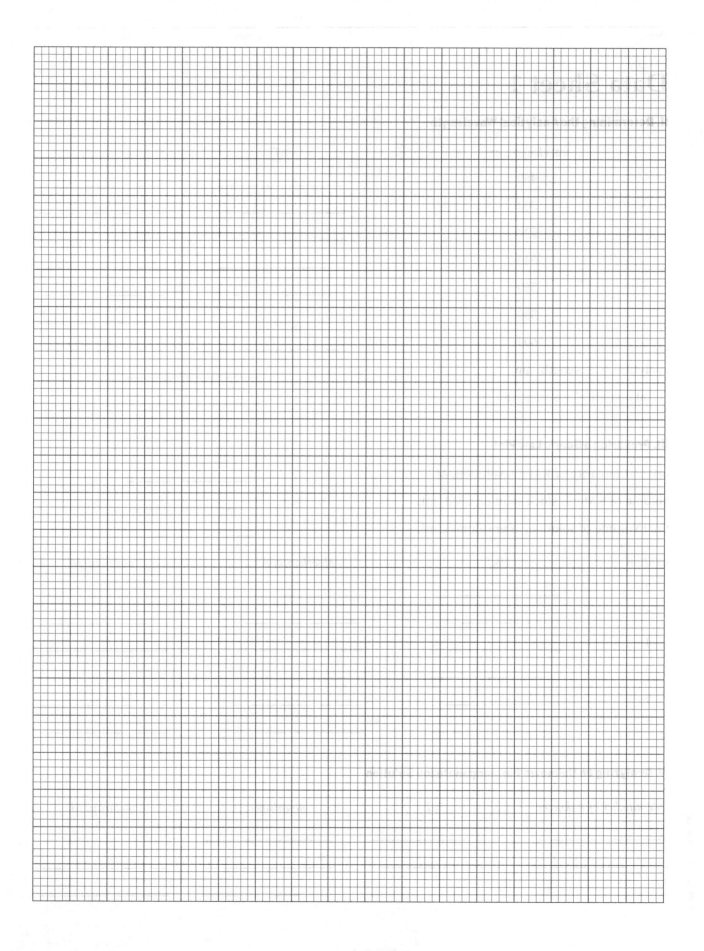

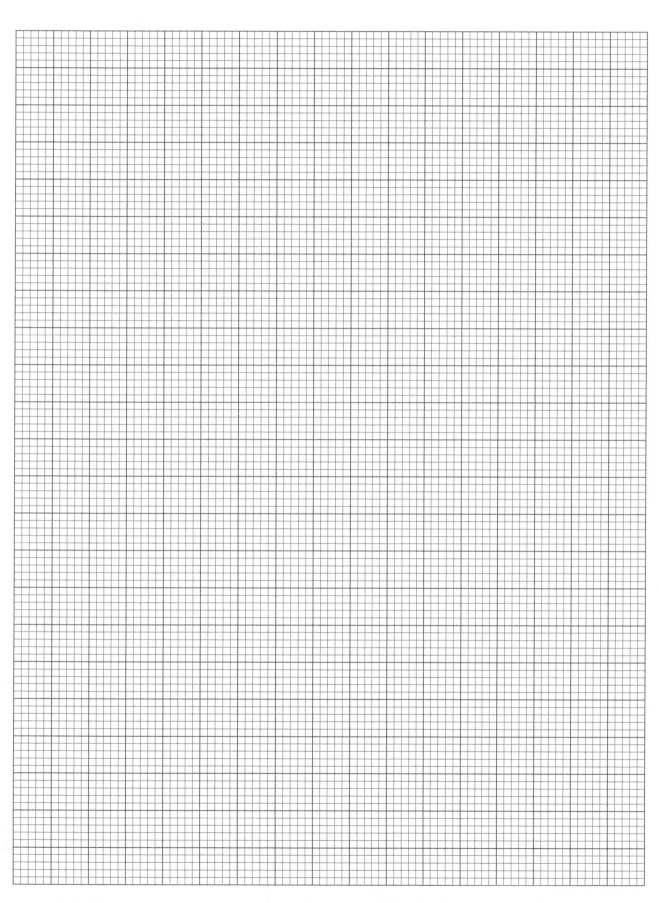

_____   _____   _____

Pre-Laboratory Assignment

1. Read an authoritative source for a discussion of spectrophotometry.

2. The two components of the solution you will be making in this experiment must be used with great care. List these two substances and describe the problems associated with each.

3. 1,10-Phenanthroline forms a bright red complex with iron(II). The complex has an analytical wavelength of 510 nm and has a high molar absorptivity. Hydroxylamine hydrochloride is added to keep the iron in a reduced +2 state, and the pH is controlled using an acetate buffer. A series of iron(II)–phenanthroline solutions were made by adding various amounts of $4.300 \times 10^{-4} M$ Fe^{2+} to 5 mL each of hydroxylamine hydrochloride, acetate buffer, and 1,10-phenanthroline. Distilled water was added to make the total volume of each solution 50.00 mL. The percent transmittance of each solution was read, using a blank containing everything but the iron(II) solution. Data for the determination are

volume of stock solution, mL	%T	volume of stock solution, mL	%T
1.00	80.35	7.00	21.78
2.00	64.71	9.00	14.09
5.00	33.65	10.00	11.32

(1) Calculate the molar concentration of $[Fe(phenanthroline)_3]^{2+}$ in each solution.

(2) Convert percent transmittances to equivalent absorbances, using Equation 4.

(3) Prepare a Beer's law plot for $[Fe(phenanthroline)_3]^{2+}$, using the data obtained in (1) and (2). Draw a best straight line through the data points.

(4) A solution containing an unknown amount of iron(II) was treated with hydroxylamine hydrochloride, acetate buffer, and 1,10-phenanthroline as described above. The percent transmittance of the sample at $\lambda = 510$ nm was 52.4 when read against a blank containing all but the iron(II) solution. Determine the molar concentration of iron(II) in the unknown.

(5) Calculate the molar absorptivity for $[Fe(phenanthroline)_3]^{2+}$. Assume a 1.00-cm path-length.

PROP *0344*

Molar Mass Determination by Freezing Point Depression in t-Butyl Alcohol

Prepared by M. Gillette and S. R. Johnson, Indiana University Kokomo

PURPOSE OF THE EXPERIMENT

Determine the freezing point of *t*-butyl alcohol, the molal freezing point constant for *t*-butyl alcohol, and the molar mass of an unknown.

BACKGROUND INFORMATION

I. The Concept of Physical States or Phases

Pure molecular substances can exist in three **physical states**, often referred to as **phases**: solid, liquid, or gas. The extent to which the individual molecules are free to move independently of each other is different in each of these states. This freedom results from the extent to which one molecule has influence on, or is influenced by, other molecules in ts immediate vicinity. The physical state of a substance depends upon two factors:

1. Intermolecular interactions resulting from hydrogen-bonding, dipole-dipole interactions, and/or London forces characteristic of the particular substance.

2. The amount of kinetic energy possessed by the molecules of the substance, which depends on temperature.

II. The Melting Point of a Substance

In the solid phase, the molecules of a substance have insufficient kinetic energy to overcome intermolecular attractions. Therefore, the substance has a rigid structure. When we heat a solid substance, the kinetic energy of the molecules increases. They begin to move with respect to one another. As we continue to heat the substance, the molecular motion becomes sufficient to cause the outer parts of the rigid structure to begin to break down, and we obtain a mixture of the solid and liquid. We call the breakdown process **melting** and the temperature at which the transition occurs, the **melting point**. Application of additional heat converts the entire sample from solid to liquid. In the liquid phase, intermolecular interactions are weaker than in the solid phase.

III. The Freezing Point of a Substance

We can reverse the melting process at any point simply by removing heat from a substance. For example, as a pure liquid cools, the molecules lose kinetic energy. At some temperature they have insufficient energy to overcome intermolecular forces, and the solid phase begins to form. We call the change from liquid to solid **freezing** and the temperature at which the transition occurs, the **freezing point**. The melting and freezing points of a substance should theoretically be the same. Because freezing and melting depend only on temperature and the particular intermolecular interactions characteristic of a substance, the freezing (or melting) point is a **physical constant** of the substance.

IV. The Freezing Point of a Solution

When we dissolve a nonvolatile **solute** in a liquid, we obtain a **solution**. The liquid in which the solute dissolves is the **solvent**. The presence of a solute affects the freezing behavior of the solvent. This is because the individual solute particles interfere with the intermolecular interactions that would establish the freezing behavior of the solvent if it were pure. Hence, the freezing point of the solvent is depressed, or lowered, by the presence of solute particles. The *identity* of the solute is not as important as is the *number* of solute particles in solution.

If the solute and solvent react, new substances are formed, resulting in a complex system that is not as easily interpreted as the one we are discussing. For our purposes, we will assume no reaction between solute and solvent.

The extent of freezing point depression caused by the presence of solute particles is different for each solvent but is always dependent on the **molality** of the solute. Molality is the number of moles of solute in one kilogram of solvent (Equation 1).

$$m_c = \frac{\text{number of moles of solute}}{\text{mass of solvent, kg}} \qquad \text{(Eq. 1)}$$

The proportionality constant relating the change in freezing point (ΔT_f) to the molality of solute particles (m_c) is the **molal freezing point depression constant**, K_f. The mathematical expression for this relationship is given in Equation 2.

$$\Delta T_f = T_f - T_f' = (K_f)(m_c) \qquad \text{(Eq. 2)}$$

where T_f is the freezing point of the pure solvent and T_f' is the freezing point of the solution. The molal freezing point depression constants for several solvents are listed in Table 1.

V. Using Freezing Point Measurements

Freezing point measurements are easy to make. We can use the relationship expressed in Equation 1 to determine the molar mass of an unknown. First, we determine the freezing point of a carefully weighed amount of solvent. Next, we add a carefully weighed amount of unknown solute to the solvent and repeat the freezing point determination. From these data, ΔT_f is calculated. By rearranging Equation 2 and solving for m_c, we obtain Equation 3.

$$m_c = \frac{\Delta T_f, °C}{K_f, °C \text{ molal}^{-1}} \qquad \text{(Eq. 3)}$$

Table 1 *Some molal freezing point depression constants*

solvent	freezing point, °C	K_f, °C kg mol^{-1}
water	0.00	1.86
acetic acid	16.6	3.90
benzene	5.50	5.10
camphor	179.8	40.0
cyclohexanol	25	39.3
cyclohexane	6.5	20.2
nitrobenzene	5.25	6.87

Because Equation 1 and 3 are related to each other by the common m_c, we write Equation 4.

$$\frac{\Delta T_f}{K_f} = \frac{\text{number of moles of solute}}{\text{mass of solvent}} \qquad \text{(Eq. 4)}$$

The number of moles of solute can also be found from Equation 5.

$$\text{number of moles of solute} = \frac{\text{mass of solute, g}}{\text{molar mass of solute, g mole}^{-1}} \qquad \text{(Eq. 5)}$$

Because Equations 1 and 5 each have the term "number of moles of solute," we substitute Equation 5 into Equation 1 and obtain Equation 6.

$$m_c = \frac{(\text{mass of solute, g})}{(\text{molar mass, g mole}^{-1})(\text{mass of solvent, kg})} \qquad \text{(Eq. 6)}$$

Then we combine Equation 3 and 6, as a result of the common m_c, and obtain Equation 7. Now our experimental data provide the necessary information to determine the molar mass of an unknown compound, using Equation 7.

$$\text{gram molar mass of solute g mole}^{-1} = \frac{(\text{mass solute, g})(K_f, \text{°C kg solvent per mole solute})}{(\text{mass of solvent, kg})\ (\Delta T_f, \text{°C})} \qquad \text{(Eq. 7)}$$

Consider the following example. Suppose you dissolved 30.9 g of an unknown solute in 500 g of cyclohexane and found that the freezing point of the mixture was 8.17 °C lower than that of pure cyclohexane. What is the molar mass of the unknown? Substituting the experimental data into Equation 7, we have

$$\text{gram molar mass of unknown} = \frac{(20.2\,\text{°C kg mol}^{-1})(30.9\ \text{g})}{(8.17\,\text{°C})(5.00 \times 10^{-1}\ \text{kg})}$$

$$= 153\ \text{g mol}^{-1}$$

VI. Colligative Properties

The proper interpretation of results obtained using the above method of molar mass determination depends upon a clear understanding of the principles involved. The depression of the freezing point of a solvent depends on the number of solute particles in the solution which is indicated by the molality of particles in the solution. Often, we think of molecules as single particles, so we assume that 1 gram-molar mass of solute is equivalent to 1 mol or 6.022×10^{23} particles of solute. This is not always the case, however. Some substances dissociate or associate in a solvent. In such cases, 1 mol of solute does not produce 1 mol of dissolved particles.

Consider a 1.00×10^{-3} molal aqueous solution of NaCl. What occurs when NaCl is dissolved in water? Equation 8 describes this process.

$$NaCl(s) \xrightarrow{H_2O} Na^+(aq) + Cl^-(aq) \qquad \text{(Eq. 8)}$$

The molar mass of NaCl is 58.5 g mol^{-1}. When we dissolve 0.0585 g NaCl in 1.00 kg H_2O, we find that we have prepared a solution that acts like a 2.00×10^{-3} molal solution in terms of its freezing point behavior, even though it is actually a 1.00×10^{-3} molal solution in terms of the number of moles of NaCl present. This difference occurs because 1 mol of NaCl dissociates into 2 mol of ions in water.

The necessity of considering the number of solute particles and not simply the molality of the solute is emphasized by the variable m_c in Equation 1. The subscript c refers to the word **colligative**. **Colligative properties**, such as freezing point, are properties of solutions that are affected by the number of solute particles present, regardless of their identity. Thus, Na$^+$ and Cl$^-$ ions have identical effects on the freezing point of an NaCl solution. Some other colligative properties are boiling point elevation, vapor pressure lowering, and osmotic pressure.

VII. Determining the Molar Mass of the Unknown in this Experiment

In this experiment, you will cool a known mass of t-butyl alcohol and measure its temperature as it changes with time. Note that as with most organic materials, contact with liquid t-butyl alcohol or its vapors should be avoided since both are irritating and flammable. You will plot these data and prepare a graph similar to the one shown in Figure 1.

In Figure 1, you can see that the temperature decreases as the liquid cools and then remains almost constant once freezing begins and both the liquid and solid phases are present. Frequently, there is a dip (see Figure 1) in the temperature curve at the freezing point. The dip is due to supercooling and should be ignored when determining the freezing point. Straight lines are fit to the liquid and liquid-solid portions of the curve and the latter is extrapolated to find the freezing point, T_f.

You will then add a known mass of water to the sample of t-butyl alcohol and collect temperature–time data for the cooling of this solution. From these data, you will determine the molal freezing point constant of t-butyl alcohol, using Equation 9.

$$K_f = \frac{\Delta T_f}{m_c} \qquad \text{(Eq. 9)}$$

Finally, you will add a known mass or volume of your assigned unknown to a sample of t-butyl alcohol and cool the solution while

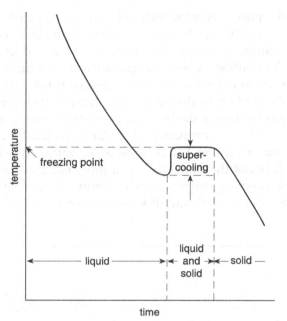

Figure 1
Cooling curve for a liquid solvent

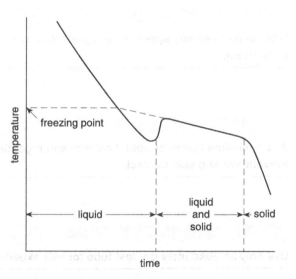

Figure 2
Cooling curve for a typical solution

collecting time–temperature data. You can measure the volume of liquid unknowns with a pipet or buret and then calculate the mass of the sample, using the density of the unknown and Equation 10.

$$\text{mass of unknown, g} = (\text{volume of unknown, mL})(\text{density of unknown, g mL}^{-1}) \qquad \text{(Eq. 10)}$$

From these data, you will determine the molar mass of your unknown.

Figure 2 shows a typical cooling curve for a solution. Care must be taken in analyzing this type of curve. Notice that the portion of the curve representing the liquid-solid mixture has a negative slope unlike the case of the pure solvent shown in Figure 1. This difference occurs because, as the solvent freezes from the solution, the molality of the solute in the remaining solution increases. This increase causes a decrease in the freezing point of the solution. A best straight line is drawn through the data points. This line is extended to the left until it intersects the portion of the curve representing the cooling of the liquid. The temperature corresponding to this point of intersection is the freezing point of the solution, T_f.

The determination of molar mass hinges on the accuracy with which you determine ΔT_f. Because of the variation in temperature measured with different thermometers, you must use the same thermometer to measure the cooling temperatures of t-butyl alcohol, of your solution of water and t-butyl alcohol, and of your solution of t-butyl alcohol and unknown.

PROCEDURE

CHEMICAL ALERT

t-butyl alcohol—flammable and irritant

CAUTION

Wear departmentally approved eye protection while doing this experiment.

I. Determining the Freezing Temperature of t-Butyl Alcohol

CAUTION

Avoid inhaling fumes of t-butyl alcohol and ingesting the substance. Prevent eye and skin contact.

CAUTION

Use only an absolutely dry test tube for this experiment.

Weigh a large test tube in a 250-mL Erlenmeyer flask to the nearest 0.1 g. Record this mass on Data Sheet 4. Measure $25\,\text{mL} \pm 1$ mL of t-butyl alcohol in a graduated cylinder and transfer the alcohol to the test tube. Measure the mass of the alcohol, test tube, and flask. Record this mass on Data Sheet 4.

Assemble the apparatus as shown in Figure 3. Place the thermometer so that the end of the thermometer bulb is at the midpoint of the t-butyl alcohol and so that the thermometer does not touch the side of the test tube. Adjust the stirrer so that it can be moved from the bottom of the test tube to almost the top of the liquid.

Fill the 600-mL beaker two-thirds full of cold tap water. If the temperature of the tap water is greater than 20 °C, add several small pieces

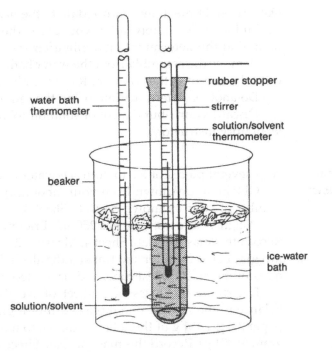

Figure 3
Freezing point determination apparatus

of ice to the water to cool it below 20 °C. Measure the temperature of the water and record the temperature on Data Sheet 1.

Immerse the test tube assembly in the cold water. Position the test tube assembly in the ice-water so that the tube is in the center of the beaker. Make certain the level of the alcohol in the test tube is 5 mm below the water level in the beaker.

Stir the alcohol continuously and steadily during the determination. Record on Data Sheet 1 time–temperature data to the nearest 0.1 or 0.2 °C every 15 s, beginning immediately after you place the test tube in the ice-water bath. End the determination 3 min after the alcohol has become slushy.

Remove the assembly from the water bath. Use your hands to warm the test tube and melt the alcohol. Raise the alcohol temperature to 25 °C.

Do another determination, using the same *t*-butyl alcohol sample.

Use this same sample for Part II.

II. Determining K_f of *t*-Butyl Alcohol

NOTE: Your laboratory instructor will inform you whether or not the class will do Part II of this experiment. If not, information will be given as to how to proceed to Part III.

Add several pieces of ice to your water bath.

Using a pipet, carefully add 0.20 mL (0.20 g) of distilled or deionized water to the sample of *t*-butyl alcohol used in Part I.

Stir the *t*-butyl alcohol and water mixture until the water has completely dissolved and the solution appears homogeneous.

Immerse the assembly in the ice-water bath. Make certain the liquid level in the test tube is 5 mm below the water level in the beaker. Constantly, but not vigorously, stir the solution and the ice-water bath. Record on

Data Sheet 2 time–temperature data to the nearest 0.1 or 0.2 °C every 15 s, beginning immediately after you place the test tube in the ice-water bath. End the determination 3 min after the solution has become slushy.

Remove the assembly from the water bath. Use your hands to warm the test tube and melt the solution. Raise the alcohol temperature to 25 °C.

Do another determination, using the same solution.

Discard your t-butyl alcohol solution following the directions of your laboratory instructor.

III. Determining the Gram Molar Mass of the Unknown

Add several pieces of ice to your ice-water bath.

Obtain an unknown from your laboratory instructor. Record the code number of your unknown on Data Sheet 4.

Weigh a large test tube in a 250-mL Erlenmeyer flask to the nearest 0.1 g. Record this mass on Data Sheet 4. Measure 25 mL ± 1 mL of t-butyl alcohol in a graduated cylinder and transfer the alcohol to the test tube. Measure the mass of the alcohol, test tube, and flask. Record this mass on Data Sheet 4.

Determine the mass of a sheet of weighing paper on an analytical balance to the nearest one thousandth of a gram (0.001 g). Weigh on this paper 2.0 g ± 0.1 g of the solid unknown to the nearest one thousandth of a gram (0.001 g). Record this mass on Data Sheet 4. Carefully transfer the solid to the test tube containing t-butyl alcohol.

If your unknown is a liquid, pipet 2.0 mL of it into the test tube containing the alcohol. Record on Data Sheet 4 the volume and the density of the liquid unknown.

NOTE: Carefully stir the t-butyl alcohol solution making certain the loop of the stirrer remains under the surface of the liquid at all times.

Carefully stir the t-butyl alcohol and unknown until the unknown compound has completely dissolved and the solution appears to be homogeneous.

Check the temperature of your ice-water bath. If the temperature is not between 14 °C and 16 °C, add several pieces of ice to the bath.

Immerse the assembly in the ice-water bath. Position the test tube as you did in Part II. Make certain the level of the solution in the test tube is 5 mm below the level of the ice-water in the beaker. Constantly stir the unknown solution and the ice-water bath. Record on Data Sheet 3 time–temperature data to the nearest 0.2 °C every 15 s, beginning immediately after you placed the test tube in the ice-water bath. End the determination 3 min after the solution has become slushy.

Remove the assembly from the ice-water bath. Use your hands to warm the test tube and melt the solution. Raise the temperature to 25 °C.

Do another determination, using the same unknown solution.

Discard the unknown solution following the directions of your laboratory instructor.

CAUTION ⚠

Wash your hands thoroughly with soap or detergent before leaving the laboratory.

CALCULATIONS

(Do the following calculations for each determination and record the results on Data Sheet 4.)

I. Determining the Freezing Temperature of *t*-Butyl Alcohol

1. For each set of time–temperature data obtained during the freezing point measurements of *t*-butyl alcohol, prepare a cooling curve by plotting temperature (ordinate) versus time (abscissa).
2. Determine the freezing point of *t*-butyl alcohol for each determination.
3. Determine the mean freezing point of *t*-butyl alcohol.

II. Determining K_f of *t*-Butyl Alcohol

4. For each set of time–temperature data obtained during the cooling of the *t*-butyl alcohol and water solution, prepare a cooling curve by plotting temperature (ordinate) versus time (abscissa).
5. Determine the freezing point of the solution.
6. Calculate the freezing point depression caused by the addition of water, using Equation 2.
7. Determine the mass, in grams, of water added ($d = 1.00$ g mL^{-1}).
8. From the mass of water added and the gram molar mass of water, determine the number of moles of water added.
9. Calculate the molality of water in the solution, using Equation 6.
10. Determine K_f of *t*-butyl alcohol, using Equation 9.
11. Calculate the mean K_f of *t*-butyl alcohol.

III. Determining the Gram Molar Mass of the Unknown

12. Prepare a cooling curve by plotting temperature (ordinate) versus time (abscissa).
13. Determine the freezing point of the mixture.
14. Calculate the depression in freezing point caused by the addition of your unknown, using Equation 2.
15. If your unknown is a liquid, calculate its mass, using Equation 10.
16. Calculate the molality of your unknown solution, using Equation 3.
17. Calculate the gram molar mass of your unknown, using Equation 7.
18. Calculate the mean gram molar mass of your unknown.

_____   _____   _____
Name   *Section*   *Date*

Post-Laboratory Questions

(Use the spaces provided for the answers and additional paper if necessary.)

1. Obtain from your laboratory instructor the gram molar mass of your unknown. Calculate the percent error for the gram molar mass of your unknown.

2. A student, following the procedure described in this module, used water as the solvent and encountered some interesting problems. Comment on the effect, if any, each of the following situations could have had on the experimental results.

   (1) The unknown, a white powder, failed to dissolve in the solvent.

   (2) The student returned to the laboratory in structor for a different solid unknown. This unknown dissolved, but bubbles were seen escaping from the solution almost immediately after the addition of the solid.

   (3) As the student was setting up the apparatus to measure the freezing point of the unknown solution, the thermometer assembly rolled off the laboratory bench, and the thermometer broke. The student obtained a new thermometer and performed the experiment as instructed.

3. A student determined the K_f of t-butyl alcohol using tap water instead of distilled or deionized water. Describe the problems that might have been encountered. How would these problems affect the magnitude of K_f?

4. As a research chemist, you are interested in studying the extent and types of interactions in aqueous salt solutions. As part of this study, you weigh three samples of NaCl and dissolve each in 1.000 kg H_2O. You then measure the freezing temperature of each solution and compare these temperatures to the freezing point of water. The data you collect are tabulated below. Explain the observed results. Predict and briefly explain the result you would expect for a solution made up of 29.22 g NaCl dissolved in 1.000 kg H_2O.

g NaCl per 1.000 kg H_2O	ΔT_f, °C
5.845	0.348
0.585	0.0360
0.293	0.0182

| Name | | | Section | Date |

Data Sheet 1

freezing point of t-butyl alcohol

determination

first　　　　　　　　　　　　　　*second*

temperature of water bath, °C　　_____　　　　　_____

	Determination				Determination	
	First	Second			First	Second
time, sec	temp, °C	temp, °C	time, sec		temp, °C	temp, °C
0	_____	_____	255		_____	_____
15	_____	_____	270		_____	_____
30	_____	_____	285		_____	_____
45	_____	_____	300		_____	_____
60	_____	_____	315		_____	_____
75	_____	_____	330		_____	_____
90	_____	_____	345		_____	_____
105	_____	_____	360		_____	_____
120	_____	_____	375		_____	_____
135	_____	_____	390		_____	_____
150	_____	_____	405		_____	_____
165	_____	_____	420		_____	_____
180	_____	_____	535		_____	_____
195	_____	_____	450		_____	_____
210	_____	_____	465		_____	_____
225	_____	_____	480		_____	_____
240	_____	_____				

Name _____   Section _____   Date _____

Data Sheet 2

freezing point of solution of t-butyl alcohol and water

determination

first _____   *second* _____

temperature of water bath, °C

time, sec	Determination		time, sec	Determination	
	First temp, °C	Second temp, °C		First temp, °C	Second temp, °C
0	_____	_____	255	_____	_____
15	_____	_____	270	_____	_____
30	_____	_____	285	_____	_____
45	_____	_____	300	_____	_____
60	_____	_____	315	_____	_____
75	_____	_____	330	_____	_____
90	_____	_____	345	_____	_____
105	_____	_____	360	_____	_____
120	_____	_____	375	_____	_____
135	_____	_____	390	_____	_____
150	_____	_____	405	_____	_____
165	_____	_____	420	_____	_____
180	_____	_____	535	_____	_____
195	_____	_____	450	_____	_____
210	_____	_____	465	_____	_____
225	_____	_____	480	_____	_____
240	_____	_____			

Name _____   Section _____   Date _____

Data Sheet 3

freezing point of solution of unknown and t-butyl alcohol

determination

first   *second*

temperature of water bath, °C   _____   _____

| | Determination | | | | Determination | |
| | First | Second | | | First | Second |
time, sec	temp, °C	temp, °C	time, sec		temp, °C	temp, °C
0	_____	_____	255		_____	_____
15	_____	_____	270		_____	_____
30	_____	_____	285		_____	_____
45	_____	_____	300		_____	_____
60	_____	_____	315		_____	_____
75	_____	_____	330		_____	_____
90	_____	_____	345		_____	_____
105	_____	_____	360		_____	_____
120	_____	_____	375		_____	_____
135	_____	_____	390		_____	_____
150	_____	_____	405		_____	_____
165	_____	_____	420		_____	_____
180	_____	_____	535		_____	_____
195	_____	_____	450		_____	_____
210	_____	_____	465		_____	_____
225	_____	_____	480		_____	_____
240	_____	_____				

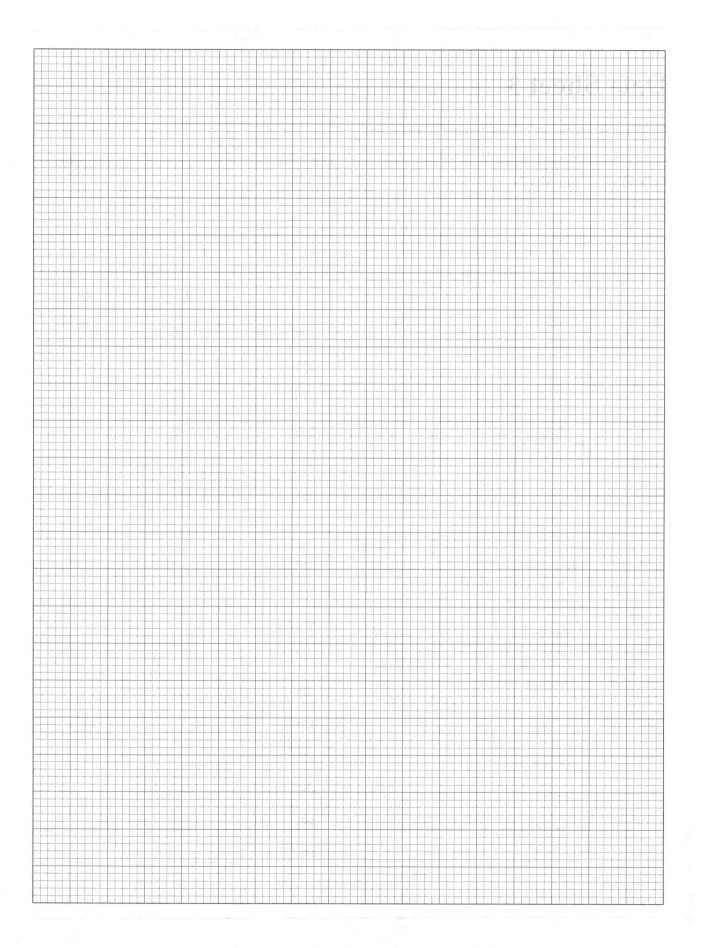

_____   _____   _____
Name   *Section*   *Date*

Data Sheet 4

I. Determining the Freezing Temperature of *t*-Butyl Alcohol

mass of *t*-butyl alcohol, test tube, and flask, g   _____

mass of test tube and flask, g   _____

    mass of *t*-butyl alcohol, g   _____

<table>
<tr><td></td><td colspan="2" align="center">*determination*</td></tr>
<tr><td></td><td align="center">*first*</td><td align="center">*second*</td></tr>
<tr><td>freezing point of *t*-butyl alcohol, °C</td><td align="center">_____</td><td align="center">_____</td></tr>
<tr><td>mean freezing point of *t*-butyl alcohol, °C</td><td align="center">_____</td><td></td></tr>
</table>

II. Determining K_f of *t*-Butyl Alcohol

mass of water, g _____

mass of *t*-butyl alcohol, g _____

<table>
<tr><td></td><td colspan="2" align="center">*determination*</td></tr>
<tr><td></td><td align="center">*first*</td><td align="center">*second*</td></tr>
<tr><td>freezing point of water and *t*-butyl alcohol solution, °C</td><td align="center">_____</td><td align="center">_____</td></tr>
<tr><td>freezing point depression, °C</td><td align="center">_____</td><td align="center">_____</td></tr>
<tr><td>number of mol of water added</td><td align="center">_____</td><td align="center">_____</td></tr>
<tr><td>molality of water in solution, m_c</td><td align="center">_____</td><td align="center">_____</td></tr>
<tr><td>K_f of *t*-butyl alcohol, °C molal^{-1}</td><td align="center">_____</td><td align="center">_____</td></tr>
<tr><td>mean K_f of *t*-butyl alcohol, °C molal^{-1}</td><td align="center">_____</td><td></td></tr>
</table>

III. Determining the Gram Molar Mass of the Unknown

mass of *t*-butyl alcohol, test tube, and flask, g

mass of test tube and flask, g

    mass of *t*-butyl alcohol, g

solid unknown number   _____   liquid unknown number   _____

mass of solid unknown and   _____   volume of liquid unknown, mL
    weighing paper, g

mass of weighing paper, g   _____   density of liquid unknown, g mL^{-1} _____

    mass of solid unknown, g   _____   mass of liquid unknown, g   _____

	determination	
	first	*second*
freezing point of unknown solution, °C	_____	_____
freezing point depression, °C	_____	_____
molality of unknown solution, m_c	_____	_____
gram molar mass of unknown, g mol^{-1}	_____	_____
mean gram molar mass of unknown, g mol^{-1}	_____	

_____   _____   _____
Name   Section   Date

Pre-Laboratory Assignment

1. Read **MISC 327, Graphical Representation of Data,** in this series or another authoritative source that describes the principles of graphing.

2. A student beginning this experiment accidentally spilled some *t*-butyl alcohol on his hands and on the laboratory bench. Describe any potential danger this situation might cause and state the proper method of cleaning up from the accident.

3. The freezing point depression of a solution of nitrobenzene and a nonionic unknown was used to determine the molar mass of the unknown. Time–temperature data for the cooling of nitrobenzene and for the cooling of a solution containing 50.0 g of nitrobenzene and 5.00 mL of a nonionic liquid unknown, are given below. The density of the unknown was 0.714 g mL^{-1}. The K_f of nitrobenzene is 6.87 °C Kg mol^{-1}.

nitrobenzene		nitrobenzene + unknown	
time, min	*temp, °C*	*time, min*	*temp, °C*
0.0	12.50	0.0	9.00
0.5	10.75	0.5	8.00
1.0	8.75	1.0	7.00
1.5	6.50	1.5	5.00
2.0	4.80	2.0	3.75
2.5	4.50	2.5	3.00
3.0	4.25	3.0	1.25
4.0	4.50	4.0	−1.25
5.0	5.00	5.0	−2.25
6.0	5.30	6.0	−2.50
7.0	5.30	7.0	−2.25
8.0	5.30	8.0	−1.80
9.0	5.30	9.0	−1.50
10.0	5.30	10.0	−1.60
11.0	5.20	11.0	−1.75
12.0	5.20	12.0	−1.80
13.0	5.20	13.0	−1.90
14.0	5.20	14.0	−2.00
15.0	5.20	15.0	−2.10
16.0	5.20	16.0	−2.20

(1) Using the graph paper on the next page, draw the cooling curve for nitrobenzene.

(2) Determine the freezing point of nitrobenzene from the curve.

_____
answer

(3) On the same graph draw the cooling curve for the unknown solution composed of 50.0 g of nitrobenzene and 5.00 mL of the liquid unknown.

(4) Determine the freezing point of the unknown solution.

_____
answer

(5) Determine the freezing point depression, ΔT_f.

_____
answer

(6) Calculate the molality of the solution, m_c.

_____
answer

(7) Calculate the gram molar mass of the unknown.

_____
answer

4. Briefly explain why it is *absolutely critical* that the test tube containing the sample of nitrobenzene be absolutely dry when determining the freezing temperature of nitrobenzene.

Studying the Rate of the Reaction of Potassium Permanganate and Oxalic Acid

Prepared by Richard C. Bell, Lebanon Valley College,
and M. L. Gillette, Indiana University Kokomo

PURPOSE OF THE EXPERIMENT

Determine the order with respect to permanganate ion and to oxalic acid concentrations for the reaction of potassium permanganate and oxalic acid solutions. Write a rate equation for this reaction. Determine the effect of increased temperature on the rate of this reaction.

BACKGROUND INFORMATION

In chemical reactions, reactant ions or molecules must collide with sufficient energy and proper orientation before their transition to product species can occur. We can learn a great deal about which collisions are most significant from a study of factors that enhance the **rate**, or velocity, with which the reaction proceeds. **Kinetics** is the study of reaction rates and of the mechanisms, or bond breaking and bond making processes, by which chemical reactions occur.

The relative proportions of reactant and product species engaging in any reaction are governed by the stoichiometry of the reaction. Therefore, the rate at which any reactant concentration decreases in the reaction mixture is proportional to the rate at which any product concentration increases. Thus, we can measure reaction rates by measuring the decrease of any reactant concentration or the increase in any product concentration. Our choice is one of convenience. For example, if only one reactant is colored, we can visually or instrumentally observe its initial presence, as well as its disappearance as the reactant is consumed in the reaction. If one reactant and one product are differently colored, we can watch the reaction mixture change color as the colored reactant disappears and the product concentration increases.

The Effect of Reactant Concentrations on Reaction Rate

Because reactions require collisions of reactant species, reaction rates often increase when the collision frequency and/or the collision energy of the reactants increases. We can increase this collision frequency in several ways. First, we can increase the reactant concentrations in the mixture. In chemical reactions involving more than one reactant, the reaction rate is often differently affected by a concentration increase of one compared to another of the reactants.

We describe the effect of such concentration increases on the reaction rate by writing the rate equation for the reaction. A **rate equation** shows the mathematical relationship between the individual reactant concentrations and the reaction rate. The relationship between an increase in a reactant concentration and the reaction rate increase (or decrease) is expressed as an exponential term called the **reaction order** with respect to that reactant. The rate equation for the reaction shown in Equation 1 takes the general form shown in Equation 2. In Equation 2, [A] and [B] represent the molar concentrations (mol/L) of A and B, x is the reaction order with respect to reactant A, y is the reaction order with respect to reactant B, and k is the **rate constant**, a proportionality constant that varies only when the reaction temperature changes.

$$A + B \rightarrow C + D \qquad (Eq. 1)$$

$$\text{rate} = k[A]^x[B]^y \qquad (Eq. 2)$$

The **overall reaction order** is the sum of the orders of the individual reactants, $x + y$ in this case. Reaction orders are usually small positive or negative whole numbers (e.g., 1, 2, −1) or fractions (e.g., 1/2, −1/2).

A. Identifying the Order of a Reaction

If a reaction rate doubles when the concentration of one reactant is doubled, the reaction rate is directly proportional to that reactant concentration. The reaction order with respect to that reactant is one, and we say that the reaction is **first order** with respect to that reactant.

Consider, for example, the reaction of nitrogen(IV) oxide (NO_2) and hydrogen chloride (HCl), shown in Equation 3.

$$NO_2(g) + 2\ HCl(g) \rightarrow NO(g) + H_2O(g) + Cl_2(g) \qquad (Eq. 3)$$

From experimental data, we find that the rate of this reaction is directly proportional to the NO_2 concentration. Therefore, this reaction is first order with respect to NO_2. We also find that the reaction rate is doubled when only the HCl concentration is doubled. Hence, the reaction is also first order with respect to HCl. The rate equation for this reaction is shown in Equation 4.

$$\text{rate} = k[NO_2][HCl] \qquad (Eq. 4)$$

The overall reaction order of this reaction is two, so we say that, overall, this is a **second order reaction**.

A reaction can also be second order with respect to the concentration of a single reactant. If a reaction rate is squared as the result of doubling the concentration of one of the reactants, the reaction is second order with respect to that reactant. For example, the decomposition of NO_2 at an elevated temperature, shown in Equation 5, has been experimentally found to be second order with respect to NO_2.

$$2\ NO_2(g) \rightarrow 2\ NO(g) + O_2(g) \qquad \text{(Eq. 5)}$$

The rate equation for this reaction is given in Equation 6.

$$\text{rate} = k[NO_2]^2 \qquad \text{(Eq. 6)}$$

We must determine the rate equation for any chemical reaction experimentally. Occasionally, the exponents of the rate equation coincide with the reactant coefficients in the balanced chemical equation, but when this happens it is a coincidence.

B. Determining the Rate Equation for a Reaction from Experimental Data

How can we use laboratory data to determine the rate equation for a reaction? Consider the reaction of sulfur(IV) oxide (SO_2) and hydrogen (H_2), shown in Equation 7.

$$SO_2(g) + 2\ H_2(g) \rightarrow S(s) + 2\ H_2O(g) \qquad \text{(Eq. 7)}$$

The rate equation for this reaction takes the general form shown in Equation 8.

$$\text{rate} = k[SO_2]^x[H_2]^y \qquad \text{(Eq. 8)}$$

We can determine the reaction order with respect to SO_2 (x) and to H_2 (y) using the **method of initial rates**. This method involves measuring and comparing the initial reaction rates when the initial reactant concentrations are independently changed. For example, consider the three determinations described in Table 1. The rate equations for these determinations are shown as Equations 9–11.

$$\text{rate}_1 = k[SO_2]_1{}^x[H_2]_1{}^y \qquad \text{(Eq. 9)}$$

$$\text{rate}_2 = k[SO_2]_2{}^x[H_2]_2{}^y \qquad \text{(Eq. 10)}$$

$$\text{rate}_3 = k[SO_2]_3{}^x[H_2]_3{}^y \qquad \text{(Eq. 11)}$$

Note that, because the reactions were run at constant temperature, the rate constant for each determination is the same. Rate data from these three determinations are shown in Table 1.

From a comparison of the results of determinations 1 and 2, we can establish the effect on the reaction rate of doubling the initial SO_2 concentration, because the H_2 concentration was held constant. We can also determine x in the rate equation by comparing the rates obtained in determinations 1 and 2. Similarly, we can compare the results of determinations 2 and 3 to determine the effect of doubling the initial H_2 concentration on the reaction rate.

Table 1 *The reaction rate of SO_2 with H_2 at constant temperature and different initial reactant concentrations*

Determination number	Initial concentration of SO_2, mol/L	Concentration of H_2, mol/L	Reaction rate, mol/L · s
1	1.50×10^{-3}	3.00×10^{-3}	4.95×10^{-7}
2	3.00×10^{-3}	3.00×10^{-3}	9.90×10^{-7}
3	3.00×10^{-3}	1.50×10^{-3}	4.95×10^{-7}

As we can see from determinations 1 and 2, the rate doubles when the initial SO_2 concentration is doubled. Because the rate is directly proportional to the SO_2 concentration, we say that the reaction is first order with respect to SO_2, and that $x = 1$. We can show this mathematically as follows. Dividing Equation 10 by Equation 9 allows us to cancel the rate constant and gives the ratios:

$$\left(\frac{\text{rate}_2}{\text{rate}_1}\right) = \left(\frac{[SO_2]_2^x \, [H_2]_2^y}{[SO_2]_1^x \, [H_2]_1^y}\right)$$

Because the $[H_2]$ was the same in determinations 1 and 2, we can cancel the two $[H_2]$ terms and simplify the ratio:

$$\left(\frac{\text{rate}_2}{\text{rate}_1}\right) = \left(\frac{[SO_2]_2^x}{[SO_2]_1^x}\right)$$

Substituting the data from Table 1 into the simplified ratio gives:

$$\frac{9.90 \times 10^{-7} \, \text{mol/L} \cdot \text{s}}{4.95 \times 10^{-7} \, \text{mol/L} \cdot \text{s}} = \frac{(3.00 \times 10^{-3} \, \text{mol/L})^x}{(1.50 \times 10^{-3} \, \text{mol/L})^x}$$

Dividing the numerators by the denominators results in:

$$2.00 = 2.00^x$$

Solving for x, we find:

$$x = 1$$

In similar fashion, we can use the data from determinations 2 and 3 to establish that $y = 1$. Therefore, the reaction is also first order with respect to H_2. Finally, we can determine that the reaction is second order overall ($x + y = 1 + 1 = 2$).

Having established the exponents for both SO_2 and H_2, we can write the rate equation for the reaction in Equation 7, as shown in Equation 12. Note that when an exponent is 1, we do not need to write it, because any number raised to the first power is equal to the number itself.

$$\text{rate} = k[SO_2][H_2] \qquad \text{(Eq. 12)}$$

We can determine the rate constant, k, by substituting the experimental rate and initial concentrations from any determination into Equation 12. For example, substituting the data from determination 1 into Equation 12, we can calculate k.

$$4.95 \times 10^{-7}\,\text{mol/L} \cdot \text{s} = k(1.50 \times 10^{-3}\,\text{mol/L})(3.00 \times 10^{-3}\,\text{mol/L})$$

Or,

$$k = \frac{4.95 \times 10^{-7}\,\text{mol/L} \cdot \text{s}}{(1.50 \times 10^{-3}\,\text{mol/L})(3.00 \times 10^{-3}\,\text{mol/L})} = 0.110\,\text{L/mol} \cdot \text{s}$$

We can now write the complete rate equation for the reaction in Equation 7 as shown in Equation 13.

$$\text{rate} = (0.110\,\text{L/mol} \cdot \text{s})[SO_2][H_2] \qquad \text{(Eq. 13)}$$

The Effect of Reaction Temperature on Reaction Rate

Molecular velocity is proportional to temperature. Thus, by increasing the reactant temperatures, we can increase the velocity of the colliding species, and hence, the energy of reactant collisions. Frequently, such an increase results in an increased reaction rate. There is a rule of thumb that, for many reactions, the reaction rate doubles with every 10-degree increase in reactant temperature. To test this generalization, we can establish the effect of temperature on the rate of a reaction. The test includes a series of rate determinations in which we vary the reaction temperature but not the initial reactant concentrations.

In this experiment, you will investigate the rate of the reaction between solutions of potassium permanganate ($KMnO_4$) and oxalic acid ($H_2C_2O_4$), using the method of initial rates. The chemistry of this reaction is very complex. For the purposes of this investigation, you may assume that the sequence of color changes from purple to red to yellow signals the end of the reaction and indicates that the $KMnO_4$ has completely reacted. You may also assume that the general rate equation for this reaction is as shown in Equation 14.

$$\text{rate} = k[H_2C_2O_4]^x[KMnO_4]^y \qquad \text{(Eq. 14)}$$

To establish the reaction rate, you will measure the time that elapses between the mixing of reactants and the disappearance of $KMnO_4$. Then, you will calculate the reaction rate using Equation 15, where $\Delta[KMnO_4]$ is the difference between the initial $[KMnO_4]$ and the $[KMnO_4]$ after the reaction takes place, and Δt is the elapsed time.

$$\text{rate} = -\Delta[KMnO_4]/\Delta t \qquad \text{(Eq. 15)}$$

You will individually vary the initial $H_2C_2O_4$ and $KMnO_4$ concentrations to establish the effect such changes have on the observed reaction rate. From these data, you will propose a rate equation for this reaction. You will also perform the reaction at several temperatures to determine the effect of temperature on the reaction rate.

In each determination you do, you will mix distilled or deionized water with $KMnO_4$ and $H_2C_2O_4$ solutions of predetermined concentrations. Thus, you will dilute the $KMnO_4$ and $H_2C_2O_4$ solutions from their original concentrations. Therefore, you will have to calculate the initial concentrations of these reagents at the beginning of each reaction.

PROCEDURE

Preview

- Rinse, label, and fill three burets, one each with distilled or deionized water, $0.755M$ $H_2C_2O_4$, and $0.130M$ $KMnO_4$.
- Time reactions of $KMnO_4$ and $H_2C_2O_4$ using the various solution volumes given in Table 2.
- Time reactions of $KMnO_4$ and $H_2C_2O_4$ solutions after heating the solutions to the various temperatures.

Chemical Alert

> $0.755M$ oxalic acid—toxic and corrosive
>
> $0.130M$ potassium permanganate—corrosive and oxidant

CAUTION

Wear departmentally approved safety goggles while doing this experiment.

I. Preparing to Measure Solution Volumes

NOTE: Your laboratory instructor will describe and demonstrate a satisfactory method for cleaning, rinsing, filling, delivering liquids from, and reading a buret.

1. Attach a clean, 50-mL buret to a buret clamp, and label it "Water". Fill the buret with distilled or deionized water.

CAUTION

Oxalic acid ($H_2C_2O_4$) is toxic and corrosive. Prevent eye, skin, and clothing contact. In case of a spill, immediately notify your laboratory instructor.

2. Obtain 60 mL of $0.755M$ $H_2C_2O_4$ in a labeled 100-mL beaker.

3. Attach a clean 50-mL buret to a buret clamp, label it "$H_2C_2O_4$", and rinse it with a 5-mL portion of the $H_2C_2O_4$ solution. Allow the rinsings to run through the buret tip into a 250-mL beaker labeled "Discarded $H_2C_2O_4$ Solution".
   Fill the buret with $H_2C_2O_4$. Record the *exact* concentration of the $H_2C_2O_4$ solution on Data Sheet 1.

NOTE: Your laboratory instructor will explain how you will obtain the $KMnO_4$ solution necessary for this experiment.

4. Record the *exact* concentration of the $KMnO_4$ solution you will use in this experiment on Data Sheet 1.

Table 2 *Reagent proportions for determinations 1, 2, and 3*

	Determination		
Reactants	*1*	*2*	*3*
$H_2C_2O_4$ solution, mL	5.00	10.00	5.00
$KMnO_4$ solution, mL	1.00	1.00	2.00
Distilled water, mL	6.00	1.00	5.00

5. Record the room temperature, measured to the nearest degree, on Data Sheet 1.

6. Assemble six clean, dry 20 × 150-mm test tubes in a test tube rack, a glass stirring rod, and a timer.

II. Determining the Effect of Reactant Concentrations on the Reaction Rate

NOTE: Complete determinations 1, 2, and 3, using the volumes of reactants and distilled water listed in Table 2.

Determination 1

7. Dispense, from the buret, 5.00 mL of $H_2C_2O_4$ solution into a clean, dry 20 × 150-mm test tube.

8. Dispense, from the buret, 6.00 mL of distilled water into the $H_2C_2O_4$ solution in the test tube.

Thoroughly mix the contents of the test tube by stirring with a glass stirring rod.

CAUTION

Potassium permanganate solution will discolor skin and stain clothing. Use gloves when handling this solution. Prevent eye, skin, and clothing contact. In case of a spill, immediately notify your laboratory instructor.

NOTE: To determine the initial reaction time, start the timer when you have added half of the $H_2C_2O_4$ solution to the $KMnO_4$ solution.

9. Dispense, from a buret, 1.00 mL of the $KMnO_4$ solution into a second test tube.

NOTE: As the reaction in Step 10 proceeds, the solution color will change from purple to red to yellow. Stop the timer when the last trace of red disappears and the solution is yellow.

10. Quickly transfer the $H_2C_2O_4$ solution from its test tube into the test tube containing the $KMnO_4$ solution.

Start the timer when you have added half of the $H_2C_2O_4$ solution to the $KMnO_4$ solution.

Thoroughly mix the contents of the test tube by stirring with a glass stirring rod. Place the test tube in the test tube support.

Stop the timer when the last trace of red disappears and the solution is yellow. Record in Table I on Data Sheet 1 the volume and molarity of each reactant, the volume of distilled water, and the elapsed time.

11. Repeat Steps 7–10 until you can reproduce the elapsed time to within 10 s. Record your data in Table II of Data Sheet 1.

Determinations 2 and 3

12. Follow the same procedure as used in determination 1 (Steps 7–11), using the quantities of reagents designated for determinations 2 and 3 in Table 2. Record all elapsed times in Table I on Data Sheet 1.

13. Transfer the reaction mixtures into the container labeled "Discarded Reaction Mixtures" provided by your laboratory instructor.

III. Determining the Effect of Temperature on the Reaction Rate

Determination 4

14. Fill a 600-mL beaker half full of warm tap water. Heat the beaker on a hot plate until the water temperature is 10–12 °C above room temperature. Stir the heating water to distribute the heat. Keep the water temperature constant to ±1 °C by adding ice or increasing the heat while you perform Steps 16–21.

NOTE: In Table III of Data Sheet 2, record the temperature of the water in the bath when the timer was started and the elapsed time of the reaction when the last trace of red disappears from the reaction mixture.

---

15. Dispense 5.00 mL of $H_2C_2O_4$ solution into a clean, dry 20 × 150-mm test tube.

16. Dispense 6.00 mL of distilled water into the test tube containing the $H_2C_2O_4$ solution.

Thoroughly mix the contents of the test tube by stirring with a glass stirring rod.

Support the test tube in the warm-water bath.

17. Dispense 1.00 mL of $KMnO_4$ solution into a second clean, dry 20 × 150-mm test tube.

Support the test tube in the warm-water bath.

18. After the solutions have warmed for about 10 min, rapidly transfer the $H_2C_2O_4$ solution into the test tube containing $KMnO_4$ solution.

Start the timer when you have transferred half of the $H_2C_2O_4$ solution.

Suspend the test tube containing the reaction mixture in the warm-water bath. Thoroughly stir with a glass stirring rod.

19. Stop the timer when the last trace of red disappears from the reaction mixture, leaving a yellow solution. Record the elapsed time on Table III of Data Sheet 2.

20. Repeat Steps 15–19 until you can reproduce the elapsed time to within 10 s. Record all warm-water bath temperatures and elapsed times in Table III on Data Sheet 2.

Determinations 5 and 6

21. Adjust the hot plate temperature to heat the water bath to a temperature 20 °C above room temperature. Stir the bath and keep the temperature constant, as you did in Step 14, while you perform Step 22.

22. Follow the same procedure as you used in Steps 15–20, using the quantities of reagents designated for determination 1 in Table 2. Record all elapsed times in Table III on Data Sheet 2.

23. Adjust the hot plate temperature to heat the water bath to a temperature 30 °C above room temperature. Stir the bath and keep the temperature constant, as you did in Step 21, while you perform Step 24.

24. Follow the same procedure as you used in Steps 15–20, using the quantities of reagents designated for determination 1 in Table 2. Record all elapsed times in Table III on Data Sheet 2.

25. Transfer all reaction mixtures to the "Discarded Reaction Mixtures" container.

    Drain the solution remaining in the $H_2C_2O_4$ buret into the "Discarded $H_2C_2O_4$ Solution" beaker.

    Drain the solution from the $KMnO_4$ buret into the container provided by your laboratory instructor and labeled "Discarded $KMnO_4$ Solution".

26. Transfer the solution from your "Discarded $H_2C_2O_4$ Solution" beaker into the container designated by your laboratory instructor and labeled "Discarded $H_2C_2O_4$ Solution". Wash the test tubes with soap or detergent if necessary. Rinse the burets and test tubes with tap water. Invert the burets, with stopcocks open, and place in the buret clamps to drain.

CAUTION

Wash your hands thoroughly with soap or detergent before leaving the laboratory.

CALCULATIONS

(Do the following calculations and record the results on your Data Sheets.)

II. Determining the Effect of Reactant Concentrations on the Reaction Rate

Do the following calculations for determinations 1, 2, and 3, and record the results in Table II of Data Sheet 1.

1. Calculate the initial $KMnO_4$ concentration in the reaction mixtures for each determination, using Equation 16.

initial $KMnO_4$ concentration, mol/L =

$$\left(\frac{\text{volume of } KMnO_4 \text{ solution added, mL}}{\text{total volume of reaction mixture, mL}}\right)\left(\begin{array}{l}\text{concentration of } KMnO_4 \\ \text{solution added, mol/L}\end{array}\right)$$

(Eq. 16)

2. Calculate the initial $H_2C_2O_4$ concentration in the reaction mixtures, using Equation 17.

initial $H_2C_2O_4$ concentration, mol/L =

$$\left(\frac{\text{volume of } H_2C_2O_4 \text{ solution added, mL}}{\text{total volume of reaction mixture, mL}}\right)\left(\begin{array}{l}\text{concentration of } H_2C_2O_4 \\ \text{solution added, mol/L}\end{array}\right)$$

(Eq. 17)

3. Calculate the average elapsed time, in seconds, for each determination.

4. Calculate the reaction rate for each determination, using Equation 15.

5. Calculate the reaction order with respect to $H_2C_2O_4$, x in Equation 14, using the method of initial rates.

6. Calculate the reaction order with respect to $KMnO_4$, y in Equation 14, using the method of initial rates.

7. Calculate the overall reaction order.

8. Calculate the rate constant, k, for the reaction. Use data from any single determination and Equation 12 to make the calculation.

9. Write a rate equation for the reaction of $KMnO_4$ solution with $H_2C_2O_4$ solution under the reaction conditions used in determinations 1–3.

III. Determining the Effect of Temperature on the Reaction Rate

Do the following calculations for determinations 4, 5, and 6, and record the data in Table III of Data Sheet 2.

10. Calculate the average temperature for each determination.

11. Calculate the average elapsed time for each determination.

12. Calculate the reaction rate for each determination.

13. Compute the average factor by which the elapsed time is decreased with each 10-degree increase in temperature. Divide the elapsed time for determination 4 by the elapsed time for determination 5. Divide the elapsed time for determination 5 by the elapsed time for determination 6. Average these two results.

14. Compute the average factor by which the reaction rate is increased with each 10-degree increase in temperature. Divide the reaction rate for determination 4 by the reaction rate for determination 5. Divide the reaction rate for determination 5 by the reaction rate for determination 6. Average these two results.

_____   _____   _____
name   *section*   *date*

Post-Laboratory Questions

(Use the spaces provided for the answers and additional paper if necessary.)

1. When you calculated k in the rate equation for the reaction of $KMnO_4$ solution and $H_2C_2O_4$ solution, you assumed k had the same value under the conditions of determinations 1, 2, and 3.

(a) What assumption did you make about the reaction of $KMnO_4$ solution and $H_2C_2O_4$ solution in those determinations that allowed you to consider k to be a constant?

(b) Would it be sound practice to compare the results of determinations 4–6 when calculating k? Briefly explain.

2. Do your experimental data substantiate the rule of thumb regarding the effect on the reaction rate of a 10-degree increase in reaction temperature? Briefly explain.

3. Consider the reaction that occurs when a ClO_2 solution and a solution containing hydroxide ions (OH^-) are mixed at 0 °C, shown in Equation 18.

$$2ClO_2(aq) + 2\,OH^-(aq) \rightarrow ClO_3^-(aq) + ClO_2^-(aq) + H_2O(l) \qquad \text{(Eq. 18)}$$

When solutions containing ClO_2 and OH^- in various concentrations were mixed at 0 °C, the following rate data were obtained:

Determination number	Initial concentration of ClO_2, mol/L	Initial concentration of OH^-, mol/L	Initial rate for formation of ClO_3^- mol/L · s
1	1.25×10^{-2}	1.30×10^{-3}	2.33×10^{-4}
2	2.50×10^{-2}	1.30×10^{-3}	9.34×10^{-4}
3	2.50×10^{-2}	2.60×10^{-3}	1.87×10^{-3}

(a) Use the method of initial rates to find the order of the reaction with respect to ClO_2 and with respect to OH^-. Write the rate equation for the reaction of ClO_2 and OH^- at 0 °C.

(b) Calculate the rate constant, k, for the reaction of ClO_2 and OH^- at 0 °C.

(c) Calculate the reaction rate for the reaction ClO_2 and OH^- at 0 °C when the initial ClO_2 and OH^- concentrations are 8.25×10^{-3} mol/L and 5.35×10^{-2} mol/L, respectively.

Data Sheet 1

I. Preparing to Measure Solution Volumes

concentration of $H_2C_2O_4$ solution, mol/L _____
concentration of $KMnO_4$ solution, mol/L _____
room temperature, °C _____

II. Determining the Effect of Reactant Concentrations on the Reaction Rate

Table I

Determination number	Volume of $H_2C_2O_4$ solution, mL	Volume of $KMnO_4$ solution, mL	Volume of water, mL	Elapsed time, s
1				
		average elapsed time, s		
2				
		average elapsed time, s		
3				
		average elapsed time, s		

Table II

Determination number	Calculated initial concentrations, mol/L		Average elapsed time, s	Reaction rate, mol/L · s
	$H_2C_2O_4$	$KMnO_4$		
1				
2				
3				

Order of reaction with respect to:

(a) $H_2C_2O_4$ _____

Overall reaction order _____

(b) $KMnO_4$ _____

Calculated rate constant, k, for the reaction _____

Rate equation for the reaction:

_____   _____   _____

Data Sheet 2

III. Determining the Effect of Temperature on the Reaction Rate

Table III

Determination number	Volume of $H_2C_2O_4$ solution, mL	Volume of $KMnO_4$ solution, mL	Volume of water, mL	Temperature, °C	Elapsed time, s
4					
		average temperature, °C			
		average elapsed time, s			
5					
		average temperature, °C			
		average elapsed time, s			
6					
		average temperature, °C			
		average elapsed time, s			

On average, the reaction time is decreased _____ times when the reaction temperature was raised 10 °C.

On average, the reaction rate is increased _____ times when the reaction temperature was raised 10 °C.

_____   _____   _____
name   *section*   *date*

Pre-Laboratory Assignment

1. Briefly identify the hazards you must be aware of before you work with:
   (a) $H_2C_2O_4$ solutions

   (b) $KMnO_4$ solutions

2. Briefly explain the meaning of the following terms as they pertain to this experiment.
   (a) reaction rate

   (b) rate equation

   (c) rate constant

   (d) overall reaction order

3. The method of initial rates involves substituting the initial reactant concentrations into rate calculations. When you do the experiment, you will be given $KMnO_4$ and $H_2C_2O_4$ solutions of known concentrations. Will you use these known concentrations in your rate calculations? Briefly explain.

4. Consider the reaction of ammonium ions (NH_4^+) and nitrite ions (NO_2^-), shown in Equation 19.

$$NH_4^+(aq) + NO_2^-(aq) \rightarrow N_2(g) + 2H_2O(l) \qquad \text{(Eq. 19)}$$

Solutions containing NH_4^+ and NO_2^- were mixed in various quantities and the following rate data at a constant temperature were obtained:

Determination number	Initial NH_4^+ concentration, mol/L	Initial NO_2^- concentration, mol/L	Initial rate for formation of N_2, mol/L · s
1	0.150	7.50×10^{-3}	3.04×10^{-7}
2	0.150	1.50×10^{-2}	6.08×10^{-7}
3	0.300	1.50×10^{-2}	1.22×10^{-6}

(a) Use the method of initial rates to find the order of the reaction with respect to NH_4^+.

(b) Use the method of initial rates to find the order of the reaction with respect to NO_2^-.

(c) Calculate the rate constant, k, for the reaction of NH_4^+ and NO_2^-.

(d) Write the rate equation for the reaction of NH_4^+ and NO_2^-.

Introducing Equilibrium

*Prepared by H. Anthony Neidig, Lebanon Valley College, and
J. N. Spencer, Franklin and Marshall College*

PURPOSE OF THE EXPERIMENT

Experimentally determine the effects of disturbances on chemical systems at equilibrium. Consider these effects in relation to Le Châtelier's principle.

BACKGROUND INFORMATION

Chemical equilibrium plays an important role in our lives. Many of the chemical changes involved in the metabolism of food are equilibrium-controlled processes. A number of important industrial processes involve chemical reactions that do not proceed to completion. Engineers must know how to manipulate such reactions in order to obtain the maximum yield of a desired product. A good example of an economically important equilibrium in manufacturing is the Haber process, used to produce ammonia.

Ammonia is a major fertilizer and is used in the synthesis of many nitrogen compounds. In the Haber process, nitrogen (N_2) reacts with hydrogen (H_2) to form ammonia (NH_3), as shown in Equation 1. The symbol in parentheses appearing after each substance in the equation describes the physical state of the preceding substance. The symbol (g) indicates that the substance is a gas, (l), a liquid, and (s), a solid; (aq) indicates that the substance is dissolved in water, forming an aqueous solution.

$$N_2(g) + 3H_2(g) \rightarrow 2NH_3(g) \tag{Eq. 1}$$

Under the same conditions, NH_3 decomposes into N_2 and H_2, as shown in Equation 2.

$$2NH_3(g) \rightarrow N_2(g) + 3H_2(g) \tag{Eq. 2}$$

At the same time reactants are forming products (Equation 1), some products are undergoing a chemical change to form reactants (Equation 2). The product, NH_3, is formed by the **forward reaction** (Equation 1), and NH_3 decomposes to form N_2 and H_2 in the **reverse reaction** (Equation 2). Reactions in which reactants are not completely converted to products because of the occurrence of the reverse reaction are called **reversible**

reactions. Such reactions are identified by a double arrow ($\rightleftharpoons$) in the equation describing the reaction, as shown in Equation 3.

$$N_2(g) + 3H_2(g) \rightleftharpoons 2NH_3(g) \qquad \text{(Eq. 3)}$$

Chemical systems that involve reversible reactions are in a dynamic state of constant interchange of reactant and product species. When the rate of the forward reaction (Equation 1) is equal to the rate of the reverse reaction (Equation 2), the system has reached a state of **equilibrium**. At equilibrium, the amounts of each substance in the system remain unchanged, even though the forward and reverse reactions are occurring constantly.

A change in any of the variables associated with a system at equilibrium may cause the equilibrium to be disturbed. We refer to such a change as a **stress** on the equilibrium state. When stress occurs, the system adjusts, or shifts, to accommodate the disturbance. This shift continues until a new equilibrium state is established.

We can predict the response of a chemical system at equilibrium to various stresses using **Le Châtelier's principle**. According to this principle, if a stress is applied to a system at equilibrium, the system will respond by shifting in the direction that reduces the stress, in order to reach a new equilibrium state.

Consider the effect of an increase in the amount of N_2 on the system at equilibrium shown in Equation 3. The added N_2 creates a stress on the equilibrium state. We can qualitatively describe the system's response to the added N_2, using Le Châtelier's principle. To reduce the stress, some of the added N_2 reacts with H_2 to form additional NH_3. Consequently, when a new equilibrium state is established, there is a greater amount of NH_3 than was present in the original equilibrium state. We commonly say that the addition of N_2 to the equilibrium system causes the equilibrium *to shift to the right*; that is, the amount of products increases and the amount of reactants decreases. This shift continues until the rates of the forward and reverse reactions are again equal and a new equilibrium state is reached.

On the other hand, if we add NH_3 to the system at equilibrium shown in Equation 3, the equilibrium will shift to the *left*. When the system reaches its new equilibrium state, it will have greater amounts of N_2 and H_2 than were present in the original equilibrium state.

Another means of disturbing a chemical system at equilibrium is to reduce the amount of one of the components. For instance, we could reduce the amount of NH_3 in the system at equilibrium represented by Equation 3. The system would respond by shifting to the right, to replenish NH_3 and establish a new equilibrium state. In the Haber process, the yield of NH_3 is increased by removing the NH_3 as it forms.

Another stress on a chemical system at equilibrium is a change in temperature. Such a change can be considered to be equivalent to adding or removing heat from the system. If the forward reaction is **exothermic**, meaning that heat is released as a product of the forward reaction, a temperature increase will cause the equilibrium to shift to the left. If the reaction is **endothermic**, meaning that heat is absorbed as a reactant in the forward reaction, a temperature increase will cause the equilibrium to shift to the right.

For example, the reaction in Equation 3 is exothermic. Heat is released as a product of the forward reaction. A temperature increase causes the equilibrium to shift to the left, resulting in a reduced amount of NH_3 and increased amounts of N_2 and H_2.

In this experiment, you will study the responses of several chemical systems at equilibrium to different kinds of stress. First, you will consider the equilibrium between chromate ion (CrO_4^{2-}) and dichromate ion ($Cr_2O_7^{2-}$). The **net ionic equation** for this equilibrium, which shows only the reacting species, is given in Equation 4. This system is formed by dissolving potassium chromate (K_2CrO_4) in water.

$$2\,CrO_4^{2-}(aq, \text{yellow}) + 2\,H_3O^+(aq) \rightleftharpoons Cr_2O_7^{2-}(aq, \text{orange}) + 3\,H_2O(l) \qquad \text{(Eq. 4)}$$

You will observe the effects of separately adding sulfuric acid solution (H_2SO_4) and sodium hydroxide solution (NaOH) to the system. An important factor in your study is the fact that hydroxide ion (OH^-) reacts with hydronium ion (H_3O^+) to form water, according to the net ionic equation in Equation 5.

$$OH^-(aq) + H_3O^+(aq) \rightleftharpoons 2\,H_2O(l) \qquad \text{(Eq. 5)}$$

Next, you will study the dissociation equilibrium of acetic acid (CH_3COOH), a weak acid, in water. The dissociation is described in Equation 6.

$$CH_3COOH(aq) + H_2O(l) \rightleftharpoons CH_3COO^-(aq) + H_3O^+(aq) \qquad \text{(Eq. 6)}$$

Because all of the components in this system are colorless, you will add methyl orange indicator to the equilibrium mixture in order to visualize the chemical changes that occur as a result of stress. Methyl orange turns red in the presence of high concentrations of H_3O^+ ion and turns yellow in lower concentrations of H_3O^+ ion. By observing color changes in the equilibrium mixture, you will determine the effect of adding water-soluble sodium acetate trihydrate ($CH_3COONa \cdot 3\,H_2O$) to the equilibrium mixture. Then you will observe the effect of adding NaOH solution to another sample of the equilibrium mixture.

The third equilibrium you will study involves two complex ions formed by the cobalt(II) ion, (Co^{2+}, or cobaltous ion). The net ionic equation for this equilibrium is given in Equation 7. This equilibrium mixture is formed by dissolving cobalt(II) chloride ($CoCl_2$) in water, forming tetrachlorocobalt(II) ion, $[CoCl_4]^{2-}$, which in turn reacts with excess water to form hexaaquo-cobalt(II) ion, $[Co(H_2O)_6]^{2+}$.

$$[CoCl_4]^{2-}(aq, \text{blue}) + 6\,H_2O(l) \rightleftharpoons [Co(H_2O)_6]^{2+}(aq, \text{pink}) + 4\,Cl^-(aq) \qquad \text{(Eq. 7)}$$

You will determine the responses of this system at equilibrium to the separate additions of hydrochloric acid solution (HCl) and water.

Finally, you will study the dissolution equilibrium of the salt, ammonium chloride (NH_4Cl) in water, as shown by Equation 8.

$$NH_4Cl(s) \rightleftharpoons NH_4^+(aq) + Cl^-(aq) \qquad \text{(Eq. 8)}$$

Starting with a saturated solution of NH_4Cl at equilibrium, you will determine the effect of the addition of HCl solution and the effects of heating and cooling the mixture.

PROCEDURE

CAUTION

Wear departmentally approved eye protection while doing this experiment.

I. Studying the CrO_4^{2-} Ion/ $Cr_2O_7^{2-}$ Ion Equilibrium

NOTE: The numbers appearing in parentheses indicate the specific lines on your Data Sheet on which the indicated data should be entered.

CAUTION

Potassium chromate is a suspected carcinogen and mutagen, but a K_2CrO_4 solution can be used safely when handled prudently. Avoid skin contact. Thoroughly wash your hands with soap or detergent after using the solution. If you spill any of the solution, immediately notify your laboratory instructor.

1. Measure 3 mL of 0.1*M* K_2CrO_4 solution in a clean, 10-mL graduated cylinder and pour the solution into a clean test tube.
   Record the color of the solution on your Data Sheet (1).

CAUTION

3*M* H_2SO_4 solution is toxic, corrosive, and can cause severe burns.
Prevent contact with your eyes, skin, clothing, and combustible material. Avoid ingesting the solution. If you spill any solution, immediately notify your laboratory instructor.

2. Add one drop of 3*M* H_2SO_4 solution to the K_2CrO_4 solution in the test tube (Step 1), while stirring with a clean, dry, glass stirring rod. Continue adding H_2SO_4 solution dropwise, stirring after each addition, until you observe a color change in the equilibrium mixture. Leave the stirring rod in the test tube.
   Record your observations on your Data Sheet (2).

3. Add one drop of 1M NaOH solution to the equilibrium mixture in the test tube (Step 2), while stirring. Continue adding NaOH solution dropwise, stirring after each addition, until you observe a change in the equilibrium mixture.

    Record your observations on your Data Sheet (3).

4. Label a 150-mL beaker "Discarded Mixtures and Rinses." Pour the equilibrium mixture (Step 3) into the labeled beaker. Rinse the graduated cylinder and the test tube with 3–5 mL of tap water each. Pour the rinses into the labeled beaker. Then rinse the cylinder and test tube twice each with 5 mL of distilled or deionized water. Pour the rinses into the beaker.

5. Transfer the contents of the 150-mL beaker into the container specified by your laboratory instructor and labeled "Discarded Chromate–Dichromate Equilibrium Mixtures." Rinse the beaker with 5 mL of distilled water, and pour the rinse into the same discard container.

NOTE: At this point, your laboratory instructor may ask you to answer Questions 4–8 on your Data Sheet. If not, proceed to Step 6.

II. Studying the Dissociation of CH$_3$COOH in Water

6. Measure 3 mL of 1M CH$_3$COOH solution in a clean, 10-mL graduated cylinder, and pour into a clean test tube. Add 3 drops of methyl orange indicator solution to the solution in the test tube. Stir the solution with a clean, dry, glass stirring rod.

    Record the color of the initial equilibrium mixture on your Data Sheet (9).

7. Use a micro spatula to add 2 or 3 crystals of CH$_3$COONa to the test tube (Step 6). Stir the solution until the crystals dissolve. Continue to add individual crystals, stirring after each addition, until you observe a change in the equilibrium mixture. Place the test tube in a clean, 250-mL beaker or a test tube support rack.

    Record your observations on your Data Sheet (10).

8. Measure an additional 3 mL of 1M CH$_3$COOH solution into the 10-mL graduated cylinder, and pour into a second clean test tube. Add 3 drops of methyl orange indicator solution and stir. Add one drop of 1M NaOH solution to the second test tube and stir. Continue adding NaOH solution dropwise, stirring after each addition, until you observe a change in the equilibrium mixture.

    Record your observations on your Data Sheet (11).

9. Pour the equilibrium mixtures from both test tubes (Steps 7 and 8) into the 150-mL beaker labeled "Discarded Mixtures and Rinses." Rinse the graduated cylinder and both test tubes with 3–5 mL of tap water each. Pour the rinses into the labeled beaker. Then rinse the cylinder and test tube twice each with 5 mL of distilled water. Pour the rinses into the beaker.

10. Transfer the contents of the 150-mL beaker into the container specified by your laboratory instructor and labeled "Discarded Acetic Acid Equilibrium Mixtures." Rinse the beaker with 5 mL of distilled water, and pour the rinse into the same discard container.

NOTE: At this point, your laboratory instructor may ask you to answer Questions 12–16 on your Data Sheet. If not, proceed to Step 11.

III. Studying the $[CoCl_4]^{2-}$ Ion/$[Co(H_2O)_6]^{2+}$ Ion Equilibrium

11. Prepare a hot-water bath. Pour 100 mL of hot tap water into a 250-mL beaker. Add several boiling stones to the water. Heat the bath on a hot plate so that it will be boiling by the time you are ready to do Step 19.

12. Measure 3 mL of $0.1M$ $CoCl_2$ solution in a clean, 10-mL graduated cylinder, and pour into a clean test tube.
    Record the color of the solution on your Data Sheet (17).

> **CAUTION**
>
> Concentrated HCl is toxic, corrosive, and can cause burns. Prevent contact with your eyes, skin, and clothing. Avoid ingesting the substance. If you spill any solution, immediately notify your laboratory instructor.

13. Add one drop of concentrated HCl to the test tube (Step 12), while stirring with a clean, dry stirring rod. Continue adding HCl dropwise, stirring after each addition, until you see a change in the equilibrium mixture.
    Record your observations on your Data Sheet (18).
    Continue adding HCl dropwise, stirring after each addition, until no further change occurs.
    Record your observations on your Data Sheet (18).

14. Add distilled water dropwise, to the test tube (Step 13), while stirring, until a change occurs.
    Record your observations on your Data Sheet (19).
    Continue to add distilled water dropwise until no further change occurs.
    Record your observations on your Data Sheet (19).

15. Discard the equilibrium mixture (Step 14) into the 150-mL beaker labeled "Discarded Mixtures and Rinses." Rinse the graduated cylinder and the test tube with 3–5 mL of tap water each. Pour the rinses into the labeled beaker. Then rinse the cylinder and test tube twice each with 5 mL of distilled water. Pour the rinses into the beaker.

16. Transfer the contents of the 150-mL beaker into the container specified by your laboratory instructor and labeled "Discarded Cobalt(II) Ion Equilibrium Mixtures." Rinse the beaker with 5 mL of distilled water and pour the rinse into the same discard container.

NOTE: At this point, your laboratory instructor may ask you to answer Questions 20–24 on your Data Sheet. If not, proceed to Step 17.

IV. Studying the Dissolution of NH₄Cl Equilibrium

17. Measure 3 mL of saturated NH_4Cl solution in a clean, *dry*, 10-mL graduated cylinder, and pour into a clean test tube.

18. Add 1 drop of concentrated HCl to the test tube (Step 17), while stirring. Continue adding concentrated HCl dropwise, stirring after each addition, until you observe a change in the equilibrium mixture.
    Record your observations on your Data Sheet (25).

19. Using a test tube holder, place the test tube and its contents, including the stirring rod, (Step 18) into the boiling water in your hot-water bath. Carefully stir the solution in the test tube while heating for 3 min.
    Record your observations on your Data Sheet (26).
    Turn off the hot plate. Place the test tube in the 250-mL beaker.

20. Use a clean micro spatula to carefully add enough crystals of solid NH_4Cl to cover the bottom of a second clean, dry test tube.

21. Measure 5 mL of distilled water in a clean 10-mL graduated cylinder, and pour onto the solid NH_4Cl in the test tube. Stir the mixture. Feel the test tube to determine if the dissolution of NH_4Cl produces a temperature change.
    Record your observations on your Data Sheet (27).

22. Discard the equilibrium mixtures from the two test tubes (Steps 19 and 21) into the 150-mL beaker labeled "Discarded Mixtures and Rinses." Rinse the graduated cylinder and test tubes with 3–5 mL of tap water each. Pour the rinses into the labeled beaker. Then rinse the cylinder and test tubes twice each with 5 mL of distilled water. Pour the rinses into the labeled beaker.

23. Transfer the contents of the 150-mL beaker into the container specified by your laboratory instructor and labeled "Discarded Ammonium Chloride Equilibrium Mixtures." Rinse the beaker with 5 mL of distilled water, and transfer the rinse into the same discard container.

CAUTION

Wash your hands thoroughly with soap or detergent before leaving the laboratory.

NOTE: If you have not answered all of the questions on your Data Sheet by this point, your laboratory instructor will tell you when you should do so.

_____   _____   _____
Name   *Section*   *Date*

Post-Laboratory Questions

(Use the spaces provided for the answers and additional paper if necessary.)

1. A student doing the experiment in this module extended the study of the $[CoCl_4]^{2-}$ ion/$[Co(H_2O)_6]^{2+}$ ion equilibrium. In one test tube, the student added silver nitrate $(AgNO_3)$ to a blue equilibrium mixture prepared from $CoCl_2$. The reaction mixture became pink and cloudy, and a white precipitate settled out leaving a clear, pink solution. The student identified the precipitate as silver chloride, $AgCl$.

(1) Briefly explain how these observations are consistent with Le Châtelier's principle.

In a second test, the student placed a test tube containing a pink equilibrium mixture in a hot-water bath. The solution turned blue. When the student removed the test tube from the hot-water bath and placed it in an ice-water bath, the solution turned pink.

(2) Is the forward reaction in the $[CoCl_4]^{2-}$ ion/$[Co(H_2O)_6]^{2+}$ ion equilibrium exothermic or endothermic?

(3) Briefly explain how the student's observations support your answer to (2).

(4) Write the net ionic equation for this equilibrium, including heat.

2. The popular antacid, Milk of Magnesia, is a suspension of magnesium hydroxide, $Mg(OH)_2$. In water, $Mg(OH)_2$ undergoes the reaction shown in Equation 9.

$$Mg(OH)_2(s, \text{ white}) \rightleftharpoons Mg^{2+}(aq) + 2\,OH^-(aq) \qquad (\text{Eq. 9})$$

(1) What would you observe if you added an acid to an equilibrium mixture containing $Mg(OH)_2$ in water?

(2) Write a chemical equation that accounts for the effect of the added acid.

(3) Briefly explain how your answer to (1) is consistent with Le Châtelier's principle.

_____   _____   _____
Name   Section   Date

Data Sheet

I. Studying the CrO_4^{2-} Ion/$Cr_2O_7^{2-}$ Ion Equilibrium

(1) What is the color of the solution in Step 1?

(2) What change do you observe when you add H_2SO_4 solution (Step 2)?

(3) What change do you observe when you add NaOH solution (Step 3)?

(4) Write the net ionic equation for the CrO_42- ion/$Cr_2O_7^{2-}$ ion equilibrium.

(5) What, if any, experimental evidence do you have that the equilibrium is affected by the addition of H_2SO_4 solution? Briefly explain.

(6) Are your observation and explanation in (5) consistent with Le Châtelier's principle? Briefly explain.

(7) What, if any, experimental evidence do you have that the equilibrium is affected by the addition of NaOH solution? Briefly explain.

(8) Are your observation and explanation in (7) consistent with Le Châtelier's principle? Briefly explain.

II. Studying the Dissociation of CH₃COOH in Water

(9) What is the color of the initial equilibrium mixture (Step 6)?

(10) What change do you observe when you add solid CH_3COONa (Step 7)?

(11) What change do you observe when you add NaOH solution to the second test tube (Step 8)?

(12) Write the chemical equation for the dissociation of CH_3COOH in water.

(13) What, if any, experimental evidence do you have that the equilibrium is affected by the addition of solid CH_3COONa (Step 7)? Briefly explain.

(14) Are your observation and explanation in (13) consistent with Le Châtelier's principle? Briefly explain.

(15) What, if any, experimental evidence do you have that the equilibrium is affected by the addition of NaOH solution (Step 8)? Briefly explain.

(16) Are your observation and explanation in (15) consistent with Le Châtelier's principle? Briefly explain.

III. Studying the $[CoCl_4]^{2-}$ Ion/$[Co(H_2O)_6]^{2+}$ Ion Equilibrium

(17) What is the color of the solution (Step 12)?

(18) What changes do you observe when you add concentrated HCl (Step 13)?

(19) What change do you observe when you add distilled water (Step 14)?

(20) Write the net ionic equation for the $[CoCl_4]^{2-}$ ion/$[Co(H_2O)_6]^{2+}$ ion equilibrium.

(21) What, if any, experimental evidence do you have that the equilibrium is affected by the addition of concentrated HCl? Briefly explain.

(22) Are your observation and explanation in (21) consistent with Le Châtelier's principle? Briefly explain.

(23) What, if any, experimental evidence do you have that the equilibrium is affected by the addition of distilled H_2O? Briefly explain.

(24) Are your observation and explanation in (23) consistent with Le Châtelier's principle? Briefly explain.

IV. Studying the Dissolution of NH₄Cl Equilibrium

(25) What change do you observe when you add concentrated HCl (Step 18)?

(26) What change do you observe when you heat the equilibrium mixture (Step 19)?

(27) What change do you observe when solid NH_4Cl dissolves in water (Step 21)?

(28) Is the dissolution of NH_4Cl exothermic or endothermic?

(29) Write the chemical equation for the dissolution of NH_4Cl in water.

(30) What, if any, experimental evidence do you have that the equilibrium is affected by the addition of HCl solution? Briefly explain.

(31) Are your observation and explanation in (30) consistent with Le Châtelier's principle? Briefly explain.

(32) What, if any, experimental evidence do you have that the equilibrium is affected by changes in temperature? Briefly explain.

(33) Are your observation and explanation in (32) consistent with Le Châtelier's principle? Briefly explain.

(34) Write the chemical equation for the dissolution of NH_4Cl in water, including heat.

Name _____   _Section_ _____   _Date_ _____

Pre-Laboratory Assignment

1. It is important for you to be aware of the hazards associated with the substances you use in an experiment. These hazards are described throughout the Procedure in the Caution boxes. Briefly describe the hazards associated with the following:

    (1) $3M$ H_2SO_4 solution

    (2) $0.1M$ K_2CrO_4 solution

    (3) concentrated HCl

2. Briefly explain the meanings of the following terms as they relate to this experiment.

    (1) forward reaction

    (2) reverse reaction

    (3) chemical equilibrium

(4) endothermic reaction

3. Iron(III) ion (Fe^{3+}) reacts with thiocyanate ion (SCN^-) to form a red complex ion with the formula $[FeSCN]^{2+}$. The net ionic equation describing this reaction is given in Equation 10.

$$Fe^{3+}(aq, \text{ lt. yellow}) + SCN^-(aq, \text{ colorless}) \rightleftharpoons [FeSCN]^{2+}(aq, \text{ red}) \qquad \text{(Eq. 10)}$$

A student studying this equilibrium begins with an equilibrium mixture that is light pink.

(1) What change will the student observe when a solution containing Fe^{3+} ion is added to this mixture?

(2) Briefly explain how your answer to (1) is consistent with Le Châtelier's principle.

(3) Silver ion (Ag^+) reacts with SCN^- ion to form silver thiocyanate (AgSCN). What change will the student observe when a solution containing Ag^+ ion is added to the mixture?

(4) Briefly explain how your answer to (3) is consistent with Le Châtelier's principle.

EQUL 0397

pH, Acids, and Bases

Prepared by H. A. Neidig, Lebanon Valley College, and
J. N. Spencer, Franklin and Marshall College

PURPOSE OF THE EXPERIMENT

Estimate the pH of solutions of acids, bases, and salts by observing the color of several indicators in these solutions. Arrange the solutions in order of their relative acidity or basicity.

BACKGROUND INFORMATION

Acid–base chemistry plays a vital role in living systems. The condition of a living organism is strongly affected by the amount of acidic or basic material present in its environment. Hence, successful corn producers control the soil acidity in order to maximize the yield. Cosmetics manufacturers carefully control the pH of their skin conditioners. Scientists regulate the reproduction of bacteria by controlling the hydrogen ion concentration in the growing environment. Stomach acid neutralizers are in constant demand by those who overindulge.

Traditionally, solutions that tasted sour were said to be **acidic**. Solutions that tasted bitter and felt slippery were called **basic**. Thus, substances such as lemon juice and vinegar were identified as acids, and solutions of lye and caustic soda as bases.

How can we identify a substance either as an acid or a base? We definitely should not taste it! Beside the fact that the ingestion of strong acids or strong bases is extremely harmful, the taste method is only a crude technique, at best. Instead, we will analyze substances to determine the concentrations of two ions, as described below.

Consider the nature of water (H_2O), a polar covalent compound. Extensive laboratory studies have indicated that a small number of ions are present in H_2O, resulting from the reaction shown in Equation 1. We call this reaction the **dissociation** of H_2O.

$$2\,H_2O(l) \rightleftharpoons H_3O^+(aq) + OH^-(aq) \qquad \text{(Eq. 1)}$$

The symbol appearing in parentheses after each species in the equation describes the physical state of the preceding substance. The symbol (g) indicates that the substance is a gas, (l) a liquid, and (s) a solid; (aq) indicates that the substance is dissolved in water, forming an aqueous solution.

In this case, the **hydronium ion (H_3O^+)** forms when a hydrogen ion (H^+) is transferred from one H_2O molecule to another. The other species that results from this process is the **hydroxide ion (OH^-)**. Very few H_3O^+ and OH^- ions are present in a laboratory sample of H_2O. In fact, for every 500 million molecules of H_2O (5×10^8 molecules), only one H_3O^+ ion and one OH^- ion exist.

In Equation 1, we see that the dissociation of H_2O results in the formation of equal molar amounts of H_3O^+ ions and OH^- ions. Thus, in a sample containing *only* H_2O, the concentrations of H_3O^+; and OH^- ions are equal. At $25\,°C$, these concentrations are each 1×10^{-7} mol L^{-1}, or $1 \times 10^{-7}M$. Square brackets placed around a chemical symbol signify the molar concentration of that substance. Hence we say that in H_2O, **hydronium ion concentration, [H_3O^+]**, is $1 \times 10^{-7}M$.

When certain substances are dissolved in water, [H_3O^+] in the resulting solution no longer equals [OH^-]. **Acids** are substances that, when dissolved in H_2O, cause an increase in [H_3O^+]. **Bases** are substances that, when dissolved in H_2O, cause an increase in [OH^-].

For convenience, [H_3O^+] of a solution is frequently expressed in terms of the **pH** of the solution, which is defined as the negative logarithm of [H_3O^+] in the solution, as shown in Equation 2.

$$pH = -\log\,[H_3O^+] \tag{Eq. 2}$$

In H_2O, [H_3O^+] $= 1 \times 10^{-7}M$, so the pH is 7.0. Because [H_3O^+] $=$ [OH^-] in H_2O, which is neither an acid nor a base, we say that a solution with pH of 7.0 is **neutral**. Solutions with pH less than 7.0 are called **acidic**. Solutions with pH greater than 7.0 are called **basic**. The pH scale has a range of 0.0 to 14.0. The relationship between [H_3O^+] and pH is shown in Table 1.

We say that a solution is either strongly acidic or weakly acidic, depending on whether its pH is closer to 0.0 or 7.0, respectively. Similarly, we say a solution is either strongly basic or weakly basic, depending on whether its pH is closer to 14.0 or 7.0, respectively.

A practical way to evaluate the relative acidity or basicity of solutions is to compare their effect on dyes. Litmus, for example, is a natural dye that turns red in most acidic solutions and blue in most basic solutions. Paper impregnated with this dye is called **litmus paper**. Litmus paper turns red in any solution whose pH is less than 5.0. It turns blue in any solution whose

Table 1 *Relationship between [H_3O^+] and pH*

[H_3O^+]	pH	[H_3O^+]	pH
$1M$	0.0	$1 \times 10^{-8}M$	8.0
$1 \times 10^{-1}M$	1.0	$1 \times 10^{-9}M$	9.0
$1 \times 10^{-2}M$	2.0	$1 \times 10^{-10}M$	10.0
$1 \times 10^{-3}M$	3.0	$1 \times 10^{-11}M$	11.0
$1 \times 10^{-4}M$	4.0	$1 \times 10^{-12}M$	12.0
$1 \times 10^{-5}M$	5.0	$1 \times 10^{-13}M$	13.0
$1 \times 10^{-6}M$	6.0	$1 \times 10^{-14}M$	14.0
$1 \times 10^{-7}M$	7.0		

pH is greater than 8.0. In solutions whose pH is between 5.0 and 8.0, the paper turns various shades of violet, caused by the differing proportions of blue and red dye molecules present. It is extremely difficult to distinguish among the color differences when litmus paper is used with a group of solutions whose pH's are all in the 5.0–8.0 range.

A $1M$ hydrochloric acid solution (HCl) will turn blue litmus paper red, as will a $1M$ benzoic acid solution ($HC_7H_5O_2$). Based on the litmus test, we know both solutions are acidic. This does not mean, however, that the two solutions have the same pH. All we can say with certainty is that the pH of each is lower than 5.0. To establish whether the solutions are equally acidic, we need to find a dye that changes color at a pH lower than 5.0.

The dye methyl violet is yellow in solutions whose pH is below about 0.5, where $[H_3O^+] = 3 \times 10^{-1}M$, and is violet in solutions whose pH is above about 2.0, where $[H_3O^+] = 1 \times 10^{-2}M$. The exact color of methyl violet in solutions whose pH is between 0.5 and 2.0 depends on the relative proportions of violet and yellow dye molecules present.

Compounds that undergo color changes when the pH of a solution containing the compound changes are called **indicators**. In Table 2, a variety of indicators are listed, with the approximate pH range over which each changes color.

We can use an indicator to determine whether a $1M$ HCl solution is more acidic than a $1M$ $HC_7H_5O_2$ solution, as follows. Experimentally, we find that methyl violet is yellow in a $1M$ HCl solution. Therefore, the pH of the HCl solution must be less than about 0.5. The actual pH of a $1M$ HCl solution is 0.0, so $[H_3O^+] = 1M$. Methyl violet is violet in a $1M$ $HC_7H_5O_2$ solution. Thus, the pH of the $HC_7H_5O_2$ solution must be greater than 2.0, so $[H_3O^+]$ must be less than $1 \times 10^{-2}M$. These observations lead us to correctly conclude that a $1M$ HCl solution is more acidic than a $1M$ $HC_7H_5O_2$ solution.

In this experiment, you will use a series of indicators to estimate the pH of solutions of a variety of substances. Based on these findings, you will determine the relative acidity or basicity of the solutions.

Table 2 *Common indicators and their associated pH ranges*

	pH range	*color change*
methyl violet	0.5 to 2.0	yellow to violet
thymol blue	1.2 to 2.8	red to yellow
	8.2 to 9.1	yellow to blue
methyl orange	3.1 to 4.4	red to yellow
methyl red	4.2 to 6.3	red to yellow
bromcresol green	3.8 to 5.4	yellow to blue
alizarin	5.7 to 7.1	yellow to red
	11.0 to 12.4	red to purple
bromthymol blue	6.0 to 7.6	yellow to blue
phenol red	6.4 to 8.0	yellow to red
litmus	5.2 to 8.1	red to blue
cresol red	7.0 to 8.8	yellow to red
phenolphthalein	8.0 to 9.8	colorless to red
thymolphthalein	9.3 to 10.5	colorless to blue

PROCEDURE

NOTE: The numbers appearing in parentheses indicate the specific lines on your Data Sheet on which the indicated data should be entered.

I. Labeling Your Equipment

NOTE: The test tubes and beakers you label in Steps 1 and 2 should remain labeled throughout the entire experiment. If any labels come off when you wash the glassware, be sure to make and attach new labels.

1. Prepare labels for your test tubes. Write "1" on one label, "2" on the second, and "3" on the third label. Attach the labels to your three test tubes.

2. Prepare labels for your two beakers. Write "Discarded Solutions" on one label and attach it to your 250-mL beaker. Write "Discarded Litmus Paper" on a second label and attach it to your 150-mL beaker.

II. Estimating the pH of an Aqueous Solution of Nitric Acid (HNO₃)

3. Obtain 9 mL of $1 \times 10^{-2} M$ nitric acid (HNO₃) solution in a clean, dry 10-mL graduated cylinder. Pour 3 mL of the solution into each of your numbered test tubes.

    Stand the test tubes in a test tube support rack or in an empty beaker.

4. Rinse the graduated cylinder twice, with 5 mL of tap water each time. Pour the rinses into your "Discarded Solutions" container.

Rinse the cylinder once with 5 mL of distilled or deionized water. Pour the rinses into the same discard container. Dry the cylinder, following the directions of your laboratory instructor.

NOTE: Do not put pH indicator paper, such as litmus paper, directly into the solution you are testing.

---

5. Place one strip of blue litmus paper and one strip of red litmus paper on a clean, dry watch glass or glass plate. Keep the two pieces of paper well separated on the glass.

6. Dip the tip of a clean, glass stirring rod in the HNO_3 solution in one of your test tubes. When you remove the rod from the solution, a drop of solution will cling to the rod. Transfer that drop to the strip of blue litmus paper by touching the rod to one end of the paper.
   Record your observations on your Data Sheet (1).

7. Repeat Step 6, but transfer the drop from the rod to the strip of red litmus paper.
   Record your observations on your Data Sheet (2).

8. Place the used litmus papers in the "Discarded Litmus Paper" container.
   Rinse the end of the stirring rod with distilled water, while collecting the rinse in the "Discarded Solutions" container. Dry the stirring rod, following the directions of your laboratory instructor. Stand your stirring rod in your test tube support rack or in a beaker when you are not using it.

NOTE: If dropping bottles filled with indicator solutions are not available, your laboratory instructor will describe how you are to transfer drops of indicator solutions to your test tubes.

NOTE: You may find it easier to determine the color of a solution if you hold a piece of white paper behind your test tube while making your observations.

---

9. Add 3 drops of thymol blue indicator solution to the solution in test tube #1.
   Record your observations on your Data Sheet (3).

10. Add 3 drops of methyl orange indicator solution to the solution in test tube #2.
    Record your observations on your Data Sheet (4).

11. Add 3 drops of phenolphthalein indicator solution to the solution in test tube #3.
    Record your observations on your Data Sheet (5).
    Answer Questions #6, #7, and #8 on your Data Sheet (6, 7, 8).

12. Discard the contents of your test tubes into the "Discarded Solutions" container. Being careful not to remove the labels, rinse the test tubes twice with 5 mL of tap water each time, and once with 5 mL of distilled water. Pour rinses into the "Discarded Solutions" container. Dry the test tubes, following the directions of your laboratory instructor.

III. Estimating the pH of Solutions of Various Substances

NOTE: Your laboratory instructor will assign solutions from the following list for you to study.

(1) sulfuric acid, H_2SO_4

(2) acetic acid, $HC_2H_3O_2$

(3) sodium hydroxide, NaOH

(4) ammonia water, NH_3/H_2O

(5) sodium carbonate, Na_2CO_3

(6) sodium acetate, $NaC_2H_3O_2$

(7) ammonium chloride, NH_4Cl

Use the following general procedure with each solution you study, just as you did in Part II when you estimated the acidity of the HNO_3 solution.

CAUTION

NaOH and H_2SO_4 solutions are corrosive and toxic and can cause skin burns. Prevent contact with your eyes, skin, and clothing. Do not ingest the solutions. If you spill any NaOH or H_2SO_4 solution, immediately notify your laboratory instructor.

NH_3/H_2O solution is toxic, corrosive, and irritating. Prevent contact with your eyes, skin, and clothing. Permanent fogging of soft contact lenses may result from NH_3 vapors. Avoid inhaling vapors and ingesting the solution. If you spill any NH_3/H_2O solution, immediately notify your laboratory instructor.

---

13. Obtain a 9-mL portion of the assigned solution in a clean, dry 10-mL graduated cylinder. Pour 3 mL of the solution into each of your clean, dry, numbered test tubes.

NOTE: Use fresh pieces of red and blue litmus paper for each different solution you test.

---

14. Test the solution in one of the test tubes with blue litmus paper and with red litmus paper, following the procedure described in Steps 5–8.
    Record your observations on your Data Sheet (9, 10) next to the formula of your assigned solution.

15. Add 3 drops of thymol blue indicator solution to the solution in test tube #1.
    Record your observations on your Data Sheet (11).

16. Add 3 drops of methyl orange indicator solution to the solution in test tube #2.
    Record your observations on your Data Sheet (12).

17. Add 3 drops of phenolphthalein indicator solution to the solution in test tube #3.
    Record your observations on your Data Sheet (13).

18. Discard the contents of your test tubes and clean them, following the instructions in Step 12.

Proceed with the next assigned solution by repeating Steps 13–18. Record on your Data Sheet your observations for each solution tested (9, 10, 11, 12, 13).

IV. Interpreting Your Laboratory Observations

19. Answer Questions 14–21 on your Data Sheet (14–21).

CAUTION	⚠

Wash your hands thoroughly with soap or detergent before leaving the laboratory.

_____   _____   _____
Name   *Section*   *Date*

Post-Laboratory Questions

(Use the spaces provided for the answers and additional paper if necessary.)

1. Briefly comment on the effect, if any, the following procedural changes would have on the observations you made while doing this experiment.

(1) You poured too much $0.1M$ NH_3/H_2O solution into test tubes #1 and #2, leaving only 1 mL of the solution in test tube #3. You added phenolphthalein indicator solution as directed.

(2) You poured too much $0.1M$ NH_3/H_2O solution into test tubes #1 and #2, so you added 2 mL H_2O to the solution in test tube #3 to bring the total solution volume to 3 mL. You added phenolphthalein indicator solution as directed.

(3) You added only 1 drop of phenolphthalein indicator solution to 3 mL of NH_3/H_2O solution in test tube #3.

2. The identification labels fell off three test tubes, each containing a colorless solution. A student knew that one of the test tubes contained $0.1M$ HCl solution, another contained $0.1M$ NaOH solution, and the third contained 0.1% phenolphthalein indicator solution. To determine the identity of each solution, the student temporarily labeled the test tubes, "*A*", "*B*", and "*C*". The student mixed the solutions in various combinations, recording all observations in the table below.

Table 3 *Observations made after mixing three unknown solutions*

mixture	observations
(1) 1 drop "*A*" + 1 drop "*B*"	red solution
(2) solution from (1) + 1 drop "*C*"	solution became colorless
(3) solution from (2) + 1 drop "*B*"	solution turned red

Determine which original label should be attached to each of the test tubes.

3. Even people who are not familiar with the study of chemistry use the expression, "the litmus test," when referring to a test that produces an unquestionable result. On the basis of your experimental results, can you conclude that using litmus paper provides a "litmus test" for determining whether a solution is acidic or basic? Briefly explain.

_____   _____   _____
Name   *Section*   *Date*

Data Sheet

II. Estimating the pH of an Aqueous Solution of HNO₃

indicator paper or solution   *observations*

(1) blue litmus

(2) red litmus

(3) thymol blue

(4) methyl orange

(5) phenolphthalein

(6) Is an aqueous solution of HNO_3 acidic or basic?

(7) What evidence supports your conclusion?

(8) By using the information in Table 2 and the color of the indicators, estimate the pH of a $1 \times 10^{-2} M$ HNO_3 solution. _____

III. Estimating the pH of Solutions of Various Substances

$1 \times 10^{-1} M$ solutions	observations				
	blue litmus (9)	*red litmus (10)*	*thymol blue (11)*	*methyl orange (12)*	*phenolphthalein (13)*
(a) H_2SO_4					
(b) $HC_2H_3O_2$					
(c) NaOH					
(d) NH_3/H_2O					
(e) Na_2CO_3					
(f) $NaC_2H_3O_2$					
(g) NH_4Cl					

IV. Interpreting Your Laboratory Observations

(14) List each of the solutions tested that is acidic.

What evidence supports your selections?

(15) List the solutions that are the most acidic.

What evidence supports your selections?

(16) List the solutions tested that are weakly acidic.

What evidence supports your selections?

(17) Arrange the weakly and strongly acidic solutions in order of increasing acidity.

(18) List each of the solutions tested that is basic.

What evidence supports your selections?

(19) List the solutions that are the most basic.

What evidence supports your selections?

(20) List the solutions that are only slightly basic.

What evidence supports your selections?

(21) Arrange the basic solutions in order of increasing basicity.

Pre-Laboratory Assignment

1. Often solutions can be hazardous in ways that are not necessarily related to their acidity or basicity. Briefly comment on the hazards that you need to be aware of when working with:

(1) $1 \times 10^{-2} M$ HNO_3 solutions

(2) $0.1M$ NH_3/H_2O solutions

2. A student performed an experiment similar to the one that you will perform, but using different solutions from the ones that you will use. The student's data are presented in Table 4 below.

(1) Is a $0.1M$ solution of $NaNO_2$ acidic or basic?

What experimental evidence supports your answer?

(2) List the solutions studied by the student that are basic.

What experimental evidence supports your answer?

Table 4 _Student data for estimating the pH of solutions_

| 0.1M solution | indicator color | | | |
	methyl violet	_methyl orange_	_thymolphthalein_	_phenolphthalein_
NH_2OH	violet	yellow	light blue	red
HNO_2	violet	red	colorless	colorless
$C_2H_5NH_2$	violet	yellow	blue	red
$NaNO_2$	violet	yellow	colorless	light pink
$Ca(OH)_2$	violet	yellow	blue	red

(3) Using these data, compare the relative basicity of the $Ca(OH)_2$ and $C_2H_5NH_2$ solutions. Briefly explain on what basis you can or cannot make this comparison.

(4) List the basic solutions in order of increasing basicity.

What experimental evidence supports your answer?

Determination of the Equilibrium Constant for a Chemical Reaction

Prepared by Emil Slowinski; Wayne C. Wolsey; William L. Masterton, Macalester College

When chemical substances react, the reaction typically does not go to completion. Rather, the system goes to some intermediate state in which both the reactants and products have concentrations that do not change with time. Such a system is said to be in chemical equilibrium. When in equilibrium at a particular temperature, a reaction mixture obeys the Law of Chemical Equilibrium, which imposes a condition on the concentrations of reactants and products. This condition is expressed in the equilibrium constant K_c for the reaction.

In this experiment we will study the equilibrium properties of the reaction between iron(III) ion and thiocyanate ion:

$$Fe^{3+}(aq) + SCN^-(aq) \rightleftharpoons FeSCN^{2+}(aq) \tag{1}$$

When solutions containing Fe^{3+} ion and thiocyanate ion are mixed, Reaction 1 occurs to some extent, forming the $FeSCN^{2+}$ complex ion, which has a deep red color. As a result of the reaction, the equilibrium amounts of Fe^{3+} and SCN^- will be less than they would have been if no reaction occurred; for every mole of $FeSCN^{2+}$ that is formed, one mole of Fe^{3+} and one mole of SCN^- will react. According to the Law of Chemical Equilibrium, the equilibrium constant expression K_c for Reaction 1 is formulated as follows:

$$\frac{[FeSCN^{2+}]}{[Fe^{3+}][SCN^-]} = K_c \tag{2}$$

The value of K_c in Equation 2 is constant at a given temperature. This means that mixtures containing Fe^{3+} and SCN^- will react until Equation 2 is satisfied, so that the same value of the K_c will be obtained no matter what initial amounts of Fe^{3+} and SCN^- were used. Our purpose in this experiment will be to find K_c for this reaction for several mixtures made up in different ways, and to show that K_c indeed has the same value in each of the mixtures. The reaction is a particularly good one to study because K_c is of a convenient magnitude and the color of the $FeSCN^{2+}$ ion makes for an easy analysis of the equilibrium mixture.

The mixtures will be prepared by mixing solutions containing known concentrations of iron(III) nitrate, $Fe(NO_3)_3$, and potassium thiocyanate, KSCN. The color of the $FeSCN^{2+}$ ion formed will allow us to determine its equilibrium concentration. Knowing the initial composition of a mixture and the equilibrium concentration of $FeSCN^{2+}$, we can calculate the equilibrium concentrations of the rest of the pertinent species and then determine K_c.

Since the calculations required in this experiment may not be apparent, we will go through a step-by-step procedure by which they can be made. As a specific example, let us assume that we prepare a mixture by mixing 10.0 mL of 2.00×10^{-3} M $Fe(NO_3)_3$ with 10.0 mL of 2.00×10^{-3} M KSCN. As a result of Reaction 1, some red $FeSCN^{2+}$ ion is formed. By the method of analysis described later, its concentration at equilibrium is found to be 1.50×10^{-4} M. Our problem is to find K_c for the reaction from this information. To do this we first need to find the initial number of moles of each reactant in the mixture. Second, we determine the number of moles of product that were formed at equilibrium. Since the product was formed at the expense of reactants, we can calculate the amount of each reactant that was used up. In the third step we find the number of moles of each reactant remaining in the equilibrium mixture. Fourth, we determine the concentration of each reactant. Finally, in the fifth step we evaluate K_c for the reaction.

Step 1 Finding the Initial Number of Moles of Each Reactant. This requires relating the volumes and concentrations of the reagent solutions that were mixed to the numbers of moles of each reactant species in those solutions. By the definition of the molarity, M_A, of a species A,

$$M_A = \frac{\text{no. moles } A}{\text{no. liters of solution, } V} \quad \text{or} \quad \text{no. moles } A = M_A \times V \tag{3}$$

Using Equation 3, it is easy to find the initial number of moles of Fe^{3+} and SCN^-. For each solution the volume used was 10.0 mL, or 0.0100 L. The molarity of each of the solutions was 2.00×10^{-3} M, so $M_{Fe^{3+}} = 2.00 \times 10^{-3}$ M and $M_{SCN^-} = 2.00 \times 10^{-3}$ M. Therefore, in the reagent solutions, we find that

initial no. moles Fe^{3+} = $M_{Fe^{3+}} \times V = 2.00 \times 10^{-3}$ M $\times$ 0.0100 L = 20.0×10^{-6} moles

initial no. moles SCN^- = $M_{SCN^-} \times V = 2.00 \times 10^{-3}$ M $\times$ 0.0100 L = 20.0×10^{-6} moles

Step 2 Finding the Number of Moles of Product Formed. Here again we can use Equation 3 to advantage. The concentration of $FeSCN^{2+}$ was found to be 1.50×10^{-4} M at equilibrium. The volume of the mixture at equilibrium is the *sum* of the two volumes that were mixed, and is 20.0 mL, or 0.0200 L. So,

no. moles $FeSCN^{2+}$ = $M_{FeSCN^{2+}} \times V = 1.50 \times 10^{-4}$ M $\times$ 0.0200 L = 3.00×10^{-6} moles

The number of moles of Fe^{3+} and SCN^- that were *used up* in producing the $FeSCN^{2+}$ must also both be equal to 3.00×10^{-6} moles since, by Equation 1, it takes *one mole Fe^{3+} and one mole SCN^-* to make each mole of $FeSCN^{2+}$.

Step 3 Finding the Number of Moles of Each Reactant Present at Equilibrium. In Step 1 we determined that initially we had 20.0×10^{-6} moles Fe^{3+} and 20.0×10^{-6} moles SCN^- present. In Step 2 we found that in the reaction 3.00×10^{-6} moles Fe^{3+} and 3.00×10^{-6} moles SCN^- were used up. The number of moles present at equilibrium must equal the number we started with minus the number that reacted. Therefore, *at equilibrium,*

no. moles at equilibrium = initial no. moles − no. moles used up

equil. no. moles Fe^{3+} = $20.0 \times 10^{-6} - 3.00 \times 10^{-6} = 17.0 \times 10^{-6}$ moles $\tag{4}$

equil. no. moles SCN^- = $20.0 \times 10^{-6} - 3.00 \times 10^{-6} = 17.0 \times 10^{-6}$ moles

Step 4 Find the Concentrations of All Species at Equilibrium. Experimentally, we obtained the concentration of $FeSCN^{2+}$ directly. $[FeSCN^{2+}] = 1.50 \times 10^{-4}$ M. The concentrations of Fe^{3+} and SCN^- follow from Equation 3. The number of moles of each of these species at equilibrium was obtained in Step 3. The volume of the mixture being studied was 20.0 mL, or 0.0200 L. So, *at equilibrium,*

$$[Fe^{3+}] = M_{Fe^{3+}} = \frac{\text{no. moles } Fe^{3+}}{\text{volume of solution}} = \frac{17.0 \times 10^{-6} \text{ moles}}{0.0200 \text{ L}} = 8.50 \times 10^{-4} \text{ M}$$

$$[SCN^-] = M_{SCN^-} = \frac{\text{no. moles } SCN^-}{\text{volume of solution}} = \frac{17.0 \times 10^{-6} \text{ moles}}{0.0200 \text{ L}} = 8.50 \times 10^{-4} \text{ M}$$

Step 5 Finding the Value of K_c for the Reaction. Once the equilibrium concentrations of all the reactants and products are known, one needs merely to substitute into Equation 2 to determine K_c:

$$K_c = \frac{[FeSCN^{2+}]}{[Fe^{3+}][SCN^-]} = \frac{1.50 \times 10^{-4}}{(8.50 \times 10^{-4}) \times (8.50 \times 10^{-4})} = 208$$

Step 5 Continued. In this experiment you will obtain data similar to that shown in this example. The calculations involved in processing that data are completely analogous to those we have made. (Actually, your results will differ from the ones we obtained, since the data in our example were obtained at a different temperature and so relate to a different value of K_c.)

In carrying out this analysis we made the assumption that the reaction which occurred was given by Equation 1. There is no inherent reason why the reaction might not have been

$$Fe^{3+}(aq) + 2\ SCN^-(aq) \rightleftharpoons Fe(SCN)_2^+(aq) \qquad (5)$$

If you are interested in matters of this sort, you might ask how we know whether we are actually observing Reaction 1 or Reaction 5. The line of reasoning is the following. If Reaction 1 is occurring, K_c for that reaction as we calculate it should remain constant with different reagent mixtures. If, however, Reaction 5 is going on, K_c as calculated for that reaction should remain constant. In the optional part of the Data and Calculations section, we will assume that Reaction 5 occurs and make the analysis of K_c on that basis. The results of the two sets of calculations should make it clear that Reaction 1 is the one that we are studying.

Two analytical methods can be used to determine [$FeSCN^{2+}$] in the equilibrium mixtures. The more precise method uses a spectrophotometer, which measures the amount of light absorbed by the red complex at 447 nm, the wavelength at which the complex most strongly absorbs. The absorbance, A, of the complex is proportional to its concentration, M, and can be measured directly on the spectrophotometer:

$$A = kM \qquad (6)$$

Your instructor will show you how to operate the spectrophotometer, if one is available in your laboratory, and will provide you with a calibration curve or equation from which you can find [$FeSCN^{2+}$] once you have determined the absorbance of your solutions. See Appendix IV for information about spectrophotometers.

In the other analytical method a solution of known concentration of $FeSCN^{2+}$ is prepared. The [$FeSCN^{2+}$] concentrations in the solutions being studied are found by comparing the color intensities of these solutions with that of the known. The method involves matching the color intensity of a given depth of unknown solution with that for an adjusted depth of known solution. The actual procedure and method of calculation are discussed in the Experimental Procedure section.

In preparing the mixtures in this experiment we will maintain the concentration of H^+ ion at 0.5 M. The hydrogen ion does not participate directly in the reaction, but its presence is necessary to avoid the formation of brown-colored species such as $FeOH^{2+}$, which would interfere with the analysis of [$FeSCN^{2+}$].

WEAR YOUR SAFETY GLASSES WHILE PERFORMING THIS EXPERIMENT

Experimental Procedure

Label five regular test tubes (18 mm × 150 mm) 1 to 5, with labels or by noting their positions on your test tube rack. Pour about 30 mL 2.00×10^{-3} M $Fe(NO_3)_3$ in 1 M HNO_3 into a dry 100-mL beaker. Pipet 5.00 mL of that solution into each test tube. Then add about 20 mL 2.00×10^{-3} M KSCN to another dry 100-mL beaker. Pipet 1, 2, 3, 4, and 5 mL from the KSCN beaker into each of the corresponding test tubes labeled 1 to 5. Then pipet the proper number of milliliters of water into each test tube to bring the total volume in each tube to 10.00 mL. The volumes of reagents to be added to each tube are summarized in Table 1, which you should complete by filling in the required volumes of water. See Appendix IV for a discussion of the use of pipets.

Mix each solution thoroughly with a glass stirring rod. Be sure to dry the stirring rod after mixing each solution.

Method I. Analysis by Spectrophotometric Measurement

Place a portion of the mixture in tube 1 in a spectrophotometer cell, as demonstrated by your instructor, and measure the absorbance of the solution at 447 nm. Determine the concentration of $FeSCN^{2+}$ from the calibration curve provided for each instrument or from the equation furnished to you. Record the value on the Data

Determination of the Equilibrium Constant for a Chemical Reaction

Table 1

	Test Tube No.				
	1	2	3	4	5
Volume Fe(NO$_3$)$_3$ solution (mL)	5.00	5.00	5.00	5.00	5.00
Volume KSCN solution (mL)	1.00	2.00	3.00	4.00	5.00
Volume H$_2$O (mL)	___	___	___	___	___

page. Repeat the measurement using the mixtures in each of the other test tubes. For a discussion of how absorbance and concentration are related, see Appendix IV.

Method II. Analysis by Comparison with a Standard

Prepare a solution of known [FeSCN^{2+}] by pipetting 10.00 mL 0.200 M Fe(NO$_3$)$_3$ in 1 M HNO$_3$ into a test tube and adding 2.00 mL 0.00200 M KSCN and 8.00 mL water. Mix the solution thoroughly with a stirring rod.

Since in this solution [Fe^{3+}] >> [SCN$^-$], Reaction 1 is driven strongly to the right. You can assume without serious error that essentially all the SCN$^-$ added is converted to FeSCN^{2+}. Assuming that this is the case, calculate [FeSCN^{2+}] in the standard solution and record the value on the Data page.

The [FeSCN^{2+}] in the unknown mixture in test tubes 1 to 5 can be found by comparing the intensity of the red color in these mixtures with that of the standard solution. This can be done by placing the test tube containing Mixture 1 next to a test tube containing the standard. Look down both test tubes toward a well-illuminated piece of white paper on the laboratory bench.

Pour out the standard solution into a dry, clean beaker until the color intensity you see down the tube containing the standard matches that which you see when looking down the tube containing the unknown. Use a well-lit piece of white paper as your background. When the colors match, the following relation is valid:

$$[FeSCN^{2+}]_{unknown} \times \text{depth of unknown solution} = [FeSCN^{2+}] \times \text{depth of standard solution} \qquad (7)$$

Measure the depths of the matching solutions with a rule and record them. Repeat the measurement for Mixtures 2 through 5, recording the depth of each unknown and that of the standard solution which matches it in intensity.

DISPOSAL OF REACTION PRODUCTS. In this experiment, reactant concentrations are very low. In most localities you can pour the contents of the test tubes down the sink when you have completed your measurements. However, consult your instructor for alternate disposal procedures.

Name _____ Section _____

Data and Calculations: Determination of the Equilibrium Constant for a Chemical Reaction

Mixture	Volume in mL, 2.00×10^{-3} M $Fe(NO_3)_3$	Volume in mL, 2.00×10^{-3} M KSCN	Volume in mL, Water	Method I Absorbance	Method II Depth in mm		$[FeSCN]^{2+}$
					Standard	Unknown	
1	5.00	1.00	____	____	____	____	____ $\times 10^{-4}$ M
2	5.00	2.00	____	____	____	____	____ $\times 10^{-4}$ M
3	5.00	3.00	____	____	____	____	____ $\times 10^{-4}$ M
4	5.00	4.00	____	____	____	____	____ $\times 10^{-4}$ M
5	5.00	5.00	____	____	____	____	____ $\times 10^{-4}$ M

If Method II was used, $[FeSCN^{2+}]_{standard} = $ _____ $\times 10^{-4}$ M; $[FeSCN^{2+}]$ in Mixtures 1 to 5 is found by Equation 7.

Processing the Data

A. Calculation of K_c assuming the reaction:

$$Fe^{3+}(aq) + SCN^-(aq) \rightleftharpoons FeSCN^{2+}(aq) \qquad (1)$$

This calculation is most easily done by following Steps 1 through 5 in the discussion. Results are to be entered in the table on the following page. If you are using Excel, set up the table as we have, and follow the directions that follow.

Step 1 Find the initial number of moles of Fe^{3+} and SCN^- in the mixtures in test tubes 1 through 5. Use Equation 3 and enter the values in the first two columns of the table.

Step 2 Enter the experimentally determined value of $[FeSCN^{2+}]$ at equilibrium for each of the mixtures in the next to last column in the table. Use Equation 3 to find the number of moles of $FeSCN^{2+}$ in each of the mixtures, and enter the values in the fifth column of the table. Note that this is also the number of moles of Fe^{3+} and SCN^- that were used up in the reaction.

(continued on following page)

Determination of the Equilibrium Constant for a Chemical Reaction

Step 3 From the number of moles of Fe^{3+} and SCN^- initially present in each mixture, and the number of moles of Fe^{3+} and SCN^- used up in forming $FeSCN^{2+}$, calculate the number of moles of Fe^{3+} and SCN^- that remain in each mixture at equilibrium. Use Equation 4. Enter the results in columns 3 and 4 of the table.

Step 4 Use Equation 3 and the results of Step 3 to find the concentrations of all of the species at equilibrium. The volume of the mixture is 10.00 mL, or 0.0100 liter in all cases. Enter the values in columns 6 and 7 of the table.

Step 5 Calculate K_c for the reaction for each of the mixtures by substituting values for the equilibrium concentrations of Fe^{3+}, SCN^-, and $FeSCN^{2+}$ in Equation 2.

Step 6 Calculate the mean value for K_c and the standard deviation. (See Appendix VIII.)

Mixture	Initial No. Moles		Equilibrium No. Moles			Equilibrium Concentrations			K_c
	Fe^{3+}	SCN^-	Fe^{3+}	SCN^-	$FeSCN^{2+}$	$[Fe^{3+}]$	$[SCN^-]$	$[FeSCN^{2+}]$	
1	$\times 10^{-6}$	$\times 10^{-6}$	$\times 10^{-6}$	$\times 10^{-6}$	$\times 10^{-6}$	$\times 10^{-4}$ M	$\times 10^{-4}$ M	$\times 10^{-4}$ M	
2									
3									
4									
5									

Mean value of K_c _____   Standard deviation _____

(continued on following page)

B. In calculating K_c in Part A, we assume, correctly, that the formula of the complex ion is $FeSCN^{2+}$. It is by no means obvious that this is the case and one might have assumed, for instance, that $Fe(SCN)_2^+$ was the species formed. The reaction would then be

$$Fe^{3+}(aq) + 2\ SCN^-(aq) \rightleftharpoons Fe(SCN)_2^+(aq) \qquad (5)$$

If we analyze the equilibrium system we have studied, assuming that Reaction 5 occurs rather than Reaction 1, we would presumably obtain nonconstant values of K_c. Using the same kind of procedure as in Part A, calculate K_c for Mixtures 1, 3, and 5 on the basis that $Fe(SCN)_2^+$ is the formula of the complex ion formed by the reaction between Fe^{3+} and SCN^-. As a result of the procedure used for calibrating the system by Method I or Method II, $[Fe(SCN)_2^+]$ will equal *one-half* the $[FeSCN^{2+}]$ obtained for each solution in Part A. Note that *two* moles SCN_2 are needed to form *one* mole $Fe(SCN)_2^+$. This changes the expression for K_c. Also, in calculating the equilibrium number of moles SCN^- you will need to subtract ($2 \times$ number of moles $Fe(SCN)_2^+$) from the initial number of moles SCN^-.

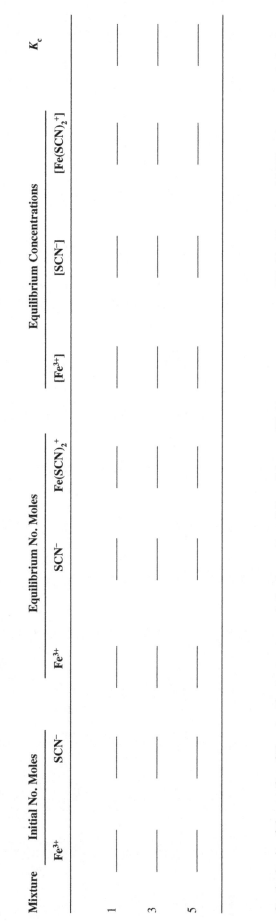

Mixture	Initial No. Moles		Equilibrium No. Moles			Equilibrium Concentrations			K_c
	Fe^{3+}	SCN^-	Fe^{3+}	SCN^-	$Fe(SCN)_2^+$	$[Fe^{3+}]$	$[SCN^-]$	$[Fe(SCN)_2^+]$	
1	___	___	___	___	___	___	___	___	___
3	___	___	___	___	___	___	___	___	___
5	___	___	___	___	___	___	___	___	___

On the basis of the results of Part A, what can you conclude about the validity of the equilibrium concept, as exemplified by Equation 2? What do you conclude about the formula of iron(III) thiocyanate complex ion?

Name _____ **Section** _____

Advance Study Assignment: Determination of the Equilibrium Constant for a Chemical Reaction

1. A student mixes 5.00 mL 2.00×10^{-3} M $Fe(NO_3)_3$ with 3.00 mL 2.00×10^{-3} M KSCN. She finds that in the equilibrium mixture the concentration of $FeSCN^{2+}$ is 1.28×10^{-4} M. Find K_c for the reaction $Fe^{3+}(aq) + SCN^-(aq) \rightleftharpoons FeSCN^{2+}(aq)$.

    Step 1 Find the number of moles Fe^{3+} and SCN^- initially present. (Use Eq. 3.)

    _____ moles Fe^{3+}; _____ moles SCN^-

    Step 2 How many moles of $FeSCN^{2+}$ are in the mixture at equilibrium? What is the volume of the equilibrium mixture? (Use Eq. 3.)

    _____ mL; _____ moles $FeSCN^{2+}$

    How many moles of Fe^{3+} and SCN^- are used up in making the $FeSCN^{2+}$?

    _____ moles Fe^{3+}; _____ moles SCN^-

    Step 3 How many moles of Fe^{3+} and SCN^- remain in the solution at equilibrium? (Use Eq. 4 and the results of Steps 1 and 2.)

    _____ moles Fe^{3+}; _____ moles SCN^-

    Step 4 What are the concentrations of Fe^{3+}, SCN^-, and $FeSCN^{2+}$ at equilibrium? What is the volume of the equilibrium mixture? (Use Eq. 3 and the results of Step 3.)

    $[Fe^{3+}]$ = _____ M; $[SCN^-]$ = _____ M; $[FeSCN^{2+}]$ = _____ M

    _____ mL

    Step 5 What is the value of K_c for the reaction? (Use Eq. 2 and the results of Step 4.)

    K_c = _____

(continued on following page)

2. Optional   Assume that the reaction studied in Problem 1 is $Fe^{3+}(aq) + 2\ SCN^-(aq) \rightleftharpoons Fe(SCN)_2^+(aq)$. Find K_c for this reaction, given the data in Problem 1, except that the equilibrium concentration of $Fe(SCN)_2^+$ is equal to 0.49×10^{-4} M.

a. Formulate the expression for K_c for the alternate reaction just cited.

b. Find K_c as you did in Problem 1; take due account of the fact that two moles SCN^- are used up per mole $Fe(SCN)_2^+$ formed.

Step 1 Results are as in Problem 1.

Step 2 How many moles of $Fe(SCN)_2^+$ are in the mixture at equilibrium? (You should use Eq. 3.)

_____ moles $Fe(SCN)_2^+$

How many moles of Fe^{3+} and SCN^- are used up in making the $Fe(SCN)_2^+$?

_____ moles Fe^{3+}; _____ moles SCN^-

Step 3 How many moles of Fe^{3+} and SCN^- remain in solution at equilibrium? Use the results of Steps 1 and 2, noting that no. moles SCN^- at equilibrium = original no. moles SCN^- − (2 × no. moles $Fe(SCN)_2^+$).

_____ moles Fe^{3+}; _____ moles SCN^-

Step 4 What are the concentrations of Fe^{3+}, SCN^-, and $Fe(SCN)_2^+$ at equilibrium? (Use Eq. 3 and the results of Step 3.)

$[Fe^{3+}]$ = _____ M; $[SCN^-]$ = _____ M; $[Fe(SCN)_2^+]$ = _____ M

Step 5 Calculate K_c on the basis that the alternate reaction occurs. (Use the answer to Part 2a.)

K_c = _____

EQUL **1005**

Solubility Product and the Common Ion Effect

Prepared by Theodore W. Tolaas, University of Minnesota

Objectives

To measure the solubility of calcium hydroxide by titrating the hydroxide produced when the solid dissolves. The solubility is determined with and without the presence of excess calcium ion in order to examine the common ion effect.

Materials

500-mL beaker, 250-mL Erlenmeyer flask, buret, buret clamp, ring stand solid $Ca(OH)_2$, 1 M HCl, *standardized* 0.1 M NaOH, 0.010 M $Ba(NO_3)_2$, 0.010 M $Ca(NO_3)_2$, 1 M HCl, bromocresol purple indicator (phenolphthalein may be used instead).

Safety

Avoid skin contact with the acids and bases. Wear safety glasses at all times during this experiment.

Waste Disposal

All the aqueous solutions may be washed down the drain with large amounts of water. Place the leftover solid $Ca(OH)_2$ in the designated solid waste container.

INTRODUCTION

You have probably studied a number of equilibrium constants, particularly those for weak acids and bases. In this experiment, you will combine what you have learned about acid-base chemistry with a determination of K_{sp}, and will use this information to study the common ion effect.

The solubility product constant, K_{sp}, is one way of describing how much of a relatively insoluble compound will actually dissolve in solution. The constant is more useful than just stating the solubility, *e.g.*, 0.014 g/L, because it can take into account contributions to cation or anion concentrations from other sources. For a compound M_nY_x, for which the equilibrium is:

$$M_nY_x \rightleftarrows nM^{+x} + xY^{-n}$$

the constant K_{sp} is defined as:

$$K_{sp} = [M^{+x}]^n [Y^{-n}]^x$$

For example, for silver sulfide:

$$Ag_2S_{(s)} \rightleftharpoons 2Ag^{+1}_{(aq)} + S^{-2}_{(aq)}$$

and the solubility product expression is given by:

$$K_{sp} = [Ag^{+1}]^2 [S^{-2}]$$

Note that in keeping with the rules of equilibrium expressions for heterogeneous systems, the solid compound does not appear.

The solubility of a solid is influenced by several factors, including the presence of other ions in solution. If the ion already present in the solution in which the solid is dissolved is also one of the ions from the solid, the solubility of the solid is decreased. For example, consider the solubility equilibrium:

$$M_nY_{x(s)} \rightleftharpoons nM^{+x}_{(aq)} + xY^{-n}_{(aq)}$$

If the species M^{+x} is added to the solution after equilibrium is established, the equilibrium will shift to the left. Therefore, more solid precipitates (or less solid dissolves), and solubility of the solid decreases. The same is true if the ion M^{+x} is in the solution *before* the solid is dissolved; the solubility is less than it is in pure water. The decrease in solubility of a slightly soluble solid in the presence of an ion that is contained within the solid is the *Common Ion Effect*. In this experiment, you will examine the solubility of a slightly soluble solid as well as the common ion effect.

One more factor must be considered. The solubility of an ionic solid also depends on other ions in the solution. That is, the solubility of AgCl will change if the solid is dissolved in solutions of varying concentrations of an electrolyte that *does not* contain either the silver ion or the chloride ion. In this case, increasing the concentration of the electrolyte causes the solubility of the solid to *increase*. This effect is the *salt effect*. In order to study the Common Ion Effect without influencing the solubility of the solid through the salt effect, the solubility of the solid needs to be measured with the same concentration of ions in all parts of the experiment. (The concentration of ions is generally measured by the quantity known as the *ionic strength*. We will not calculate the ionic strength, but we will work under conditions ensure that the ionic strength is the same in all parts of the experiment.)

Often, a compound will be so insoluble, the value of K_{sp} will be 1×10^{-16} or even smaller. This is true of many sulfides. Chemists use this fact in qualitative analysis to test for certain metal ions. Hydroxides are often only moderately insoluble. You know that sodium hydroxide (NaOH) and potassium hydroxide (KOH) are very soluble, and are useful as standard bases. This high solubility is a function of the Na^+ and K^+ cations. Going from the Group IA to Group IIA cations decreases the solubility of the hydroxides considerably. The K_{sp} for $Mg(OH)_2$ is 6×10^{-12}. A *suspension* (dissolved compound plus lots of undissolved solid floating in solution) of $Mg(OH)_2$ is familiar as the medication *Milk of Magnesia*. The suspended particles constitute the milky appearance.

Calcium hydroxide is somewhat more soluble than magnesium hydroxide. The concentration of hydroxide that will go into solution is just in the right range to be conveniently analyzed by an acid-base titration. The results of the titration will allow you to calculate the K_{sp}.

PROCEDURE

A. Preparation of Saturated Ca(OH)₂ Solutions

1. Transfer 1–2 grams of solid calcium hydroxide to a large (500-mL) Erlenmeyer flask. Fill the flask about half full with a solution that is 0.010 M in $Ba(NO_3)_2$.

2. Close with a cork or stopper and shake the solution for about 5 minutes. You will tire easily doing this, but persist. It is essential to achieve a saturated solution; that is, one where equilibrium is established.

3. Set the flask aside and keep it covered. Allow the solution to settle.

4. Repeat the above procedure using a solution that is 0.010 M in $Ca(NO_3)_2$.

B. Preparation and Standardization of the HCl Solution

1. Before you can titrate the hydroxide from the solid you must prepare and standardize a solution of HCl. Take 10 mL of the stock HCl solution (about 1 M), transfer to a beaker, and dilute to approximately 200 mL (the exact volume is not important).

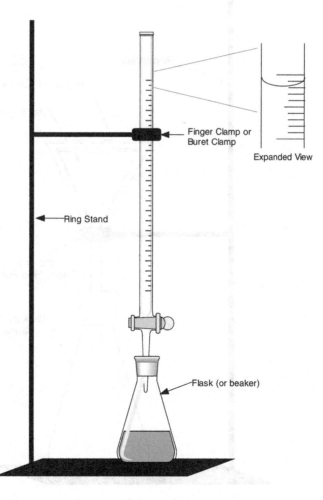

Finger Clamp or Buret Clamp

Expanded View

Ring Stand

Flask (or beaker)

2. Rinse and fill a buret with your HCl solution. A typical setup for the titration is shown on the right. Record the initial volume of HCl on your Report Form.

3. Your instructor will provide a standardized NaOH solution. (A *standardized* solution has been analyzed, and its concentration determined very precisely.) Pipet 25 mL of the standardized NaOH solution into a small (250-mL) Erlenmeyer flask. Record the NaOH concentration on your Report Form.

4. Add about 30–40 mL of distilled water, 2–3 drops of bromocresol purple indicator, and titrate with the HCl. The color change is purple (base) to yellow (acid). Record the initial and final buret readings to the nearest 0.01 mL. (If bromocresol purple indicator is not available, you may use phenolphthalein; the color change is red to colorless.)

5. Rinse the solution down the drain; repeat the standardization twice for a total of three trials.

C. Titration of the Ca(OH)₂ Solution

1. The Ca(OH)₂ solutions should have settled out by now. Take care not to stir up any of the solid from the bottom. Set up a funnel with a clean piece of filter paper and a small flask to catch the filtrate.

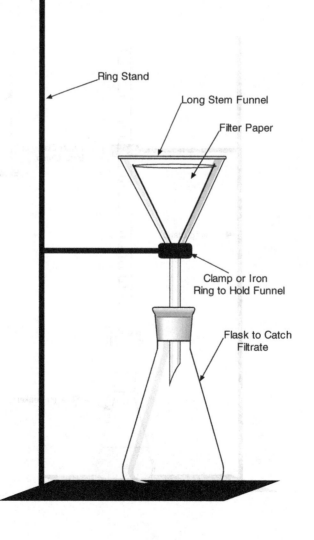

Ring Stand

Long Stem Funnel

Filter Paper

Clamp or Iron Ring to Hold Funnel

Flask to Catch Filtrate

2. Use a disposable plastic pipet to draw solution off the top of the saturated solution (or gently decant the supernatant), and transfer to the funnel for filtration. Do not allow the level of the solution to rise in the funnel above the edge of the paper. Collect 50–100 mL of filtrate and cover it. If the filtrate is still quite cloudy, repeat the filtration.

3. Pipet 25 mL of the filtrate into a clean 250-mL Erlenmeyer flask, add about 30–40 mL of distilled water and 2–3 drops of bromocresol purple, and titrate with the HCl solution that you standardized in Part B. Record the initial and final buret readings to the nearest 0.01 mL.

4. Repeat the titration twice with fresh 25 mL aliquots, for a total of three trials.

5. All solutions may be discarded down the sink. Put the undissolved $Ca(OH)_2$ in the trash.

D. Titration of the $Ca(OH)_2$ Solution in the Presence of Ca^{+2}

1. Repeat the titration described in Part C using the solution prepared in $Ca(NO_3)_2$.

CALCULATIONS

Part B: Preparation and Standardization of a HCl Solution

1. Subtract the initial volume from the final volume to get the total volume HCl used.

2. Calculate the concentration of HCl using the equation:

$$M_a \times V_a = M_b \times V_b$$

where M and V refer to molarity and volume of acid (a) and base (b).

Part C: Titration of the $Ca(OH)_2$ Solution in Distilled Water

and

Part D: Titration of the $Ca(OH)_2$ Solution in the Presence of Ca^{+2}

1. The calculations for the OH^- concentration for both Parts C and D are performed in exactly the same way as the standardization of HCl, except that now you know the acid concentration and want to calculate the concentration of OH^-.

Determination of the Solubility of $Ca(OH)_2$

2. The reaction of interest is:

$$Ca(OH)_{2(s)} \rightleftharpoons Ca^{+2}_{(aq)} + 2\,OH^{-1}_{(aq)}$$

The solubility is defined as the amount of solid that dissolves, and is commonly given in moles/liter. From the reaction stoichiometry, the solubility would be equal to $[Ca^{+2}]$ or to $1/2\,[OH^-]$. Average the $[OH^-]$ for each of the three trials in Part C, and average the three trials in Part D. Record these values in the appropriate places on your Report Form. Using these values, determine the solubility of $Ca(OH)_2$ for the solution in Part C and the solution in Part D. Record these values on your Report Form.

Calculation of the [Ca^{+2}]: The Common Ion Effect

Part C: Titration of the Ca(OH)$_2$ Solution in Distilled Water

3. You know the value of [OH$^-$] as calculated. But, what is [Ca^{+2}]? From the solution stoichiometry, it can be seen that *one* mole of calcium hydroxide produces one mole of calcium ion and *two* moles of hydroxide ion. Therefore, [Ca^{+2}] is exactly one-half [OH$^-$]:

$$[Ca^{+2}] = 1/2[OH^-]$$

Calculate the average [Ca^{+2}] from the average [OH$^-$] for the solutions in Part C.

4. Record the average [OH$^-$] and average [Ca^{+2}] for Part C on your Report Form.

Part D: Titration of the Ca(OH)$_2$ Solution in the Presence of Ca^{+2}

5. Once again, the it can be seen that when *one* mole of calcium hydroxide dissolves, it produces *one* mole of calcium ion and *two* moles of hydroxide ion. However, in this case, there is already calcium ion in solution from the 0.010 M Ca(NO$_3$)$_2$. Here, the [Ca^{+2}] is given by:

$$[Ca^{+2}] = 0.010\,M + 1/2[OH^-]$$

Calculate the average [Ca^{+2}] from the average [OH$^-$] for the solutions in Part D.

6. Calculate the value of K$_{sp}$ for calcium hydroxide for Part D from the values of [Ca^{+2}] and [OH$^-$] for Part D.

7. Compare the results for [Ca^{+2}] from Part C and Part D. Discuss.

8. Compare the values of K$_{sp}$ from Part C and Part D. Discuss.

9. Compare your results for K$_{sp}$ to a literature value. Cite your source.

Pre-Lab Questions

1. Write the K_{sp} expressions for the following equilibria:

   a. $FeS_{(s)} \rightleftarrows Fe^{+2}_{(aq)} + S^{-2}_{(aq)}$

      $K_{sp} =$

   b. $AI(IO_3)_{3\,(s)} \rightleftarrows AI^{+3}_{(aq)} + 3\,IO^-_{3\,(aq)}$

      $K_{sp} =$

   c. $Ba_3(PO_4)_{2\,(s)} \rightleftarrows 3\,Ba^{+2}_{(aq)} + 2\,PO^{-3}_{4\,(aq)}$

      $K_{sp} =$

   d. $Mg(OH)_{2\,(s)} \rightleftarrows Mg^{+2}_{(aq)} + 2\,OH^-_{(aq)}$

      $K_{sp} =$

2. Consider the magnesium hydroxide equilibrium in Question d. Solid magnesium hydroxide is added to water, and then filtered to isolate the saturated solution.

   a. What would happen to the solubility of magnesium hydroxide if the solution were made up in 0.01 M $Mg(NO_3)_2$ instead of pure water? Explain.

   b. What would happen to the solubility of magnesium hydroxide if the solution were made up in 0.01 M NaOH instead of pure water? Explain.

_____   _____   _____
name   *section*   *date*

Solubility Product and the Common Ion Effect

REPORT FORM

Part B: Preparation and Standardization of the HCl Solution

Concentration of Standard NaOH _____ M

Aliquot of Standard NaOH Used _____ mL

	Trial 1		*Trial 2*		*Trial 3*	
Final Volume:	_____	mL	_____	mL	_____	mL
Initial Volume:	_____	mL	_____	mL	_____	mL
Volume HCl	_____	mL	_____	mL	_____	mL
Molarity of HCl	_____	mL	_____	mL	_____	mL

Average concentration of HCl _____ M

Part C: Titration of Ca(OH)₂ Solution

Solution Titration—Aliquot size _____ mL

	Trial 1		*Trial 2*		*Trial 3*	
Final Volume:	_____	mL	_____	mL	_____	mL
Initial Volume:	_____	mL	_____	mL	_____	mL
Volume HCl	_____	mL	_____	mL	_____	mL
Molarity of OH^-	_____	mL	_____	mL	_____	mL

Average $[OH^{-1}]$ _____ M   Average $[Ca^{+2}]$ _____ M

Average Solubility _____ M

K_{sp} calculation (show your work and compare answer to literature value)

Part D: Titration of Ca(OH)$_2$ Solution in the Presence of Ca^{+2}

Solution Titration—Aliquot size _____ mL

	Trial 1	Trial 2	Trial 3
Final Volume:	_____ mL	_____ mL	_____ mL
Initial Volume:	_____ mL	_____ mL	_____ mL
Volume HCl	_____ mL	_____ mL	_____ mL
Molarity of OH$^-$	_____ mL	_____ mL	_____ mL

Average [OH^{-1}] _____ M   Average [Ca^{+2}] _____ M

Average Solubility _____ M

K$_{sp}$ calculation (show your work and compare answer to literature value)

Compare the solubilities in Part C and Part D, and discuss.

Compare the K$_{sp}$ from Part C and Part D, and discuss.

Post-Lab Questions

1. Convert your answers for the solubility of calcium hydroxide in Part C to grams per liter.

2. What is the pH at the equivalence point for each titration? Look up bromocresol purple indicator and explain why this is a good choice for this titration.

3. Calculate K_{sp} for $MnCO_3$ if 1.07 mg/L are required to make a saturated solution.

4. Why is it essential that the filtrate be as clear as possible?

5. Why would an acid-base titration probably be impractical for the measurement of the K_{sp} of $Mg(OH)_2$? (See introduction for a hint.)

6. The pH at the equivalence point is appropriate for the indicator bromocresol purple (see question #2 above), but it is suggested that phenolphthalein could be used instead. Look up the pH transition range for phenolphthalein, and explain why it would also be an accepted choice.

7. If the NaOH provided to you was not standardized, describe how you would go about performing the standardization.

8. If the solution is poorly filtered, the filtrate appears cloudy. Why is this? Would the K_{sp} calculated from this data be higher or lower than the true value?

9. Find the mathematical equation that is used to calculate the ionic strength of a solution. Show that the ionic strength is the same in both parts of this experiment.

The Thermodynamics of Potassium Nitrate Dissolving in Water

Prepared by Robert G. Silberman, SUNY Cortland

PURPOSE OF THE EXPERIMENT

Measure the solubility of potassium nitrate in water at several temperatures. Calculate K_{sp}, ΔG, ΔH, and ΔS for potassium nitrate dissolving in water.

BACKGROUND INFORMATION

Solubility Equilibrium

When potassium nitrate (KNO_3) dissolves in water, it dissociates into potassium ions (K^+) and nitrate ions (NO_3^-). Once sufficient quantities of K^+ and NO_3^- are in solution, however, the ions recombine into solid KNO_3. Eventually, for every pair of ions that forms, another pair recombines. As a result, the concentrations of the ions remain constant; we say the reaction is at **equilibrium**. This solubility equilibrium of KNO_3 is shown in Equation 1,

$$KNO_3(s) \rightleftharpoons K^+(aq) + NO_3^-(aq) \qquad \text{(Eq. 1)}$$

where the opposing arrows indicate that the reaction is reversible. We call this system, where undissolved solid is in equilibrium with its dissolved ions, a **saturated** solution.

We can describe the saturated solution with its fixed concentrations of ions with an **equilibrium constant** expression. Equation 2 defines the equilibrium constant, K_{sp}, for KNO_3 dissolving in water.

$$K_{sp} = [K^+]\,[NO_3^-] \qquad \text{(Eq. 2)}$$

The sp stands for solubility product and the square brackets around the ions symbolize molar concentration (M or mol/L). The equation serves as a reminder that the equilibrium constant not only is concerned with solubility but also is expressed as a product of the ions' molarities. The value for K_{sp} can be large, greater than 1, for the very soluble KNO_3, or small, less than 0.0000000001, for an insoluble compound such as silver chloride.

In addition, because the solubility of a compound changes with the temperature, its K_{sp} is likewise a function of the temperature.

Thermodynamics

We use **thermodynamics** to understand how and why KNO_3 dissolves in water. The **enthalpy** change, ΔH, for KNO_3 dissolving in water provides the difference in energy between solid KNO_3 and its dissolved ions. If ΔH is positive, heat must be added for KNO_3 to dissolve. On the other hand, if ΔH is negative, dissolving KNO_3 in water gives off heat. The **entropy** change, ΔS, for KNO_3 dissolving in water indicates the relative disorder of the dissolved ions with respect to solid KNO_3. We expect ΔS for solid KNO_3 dissolving in water to be positive because the two ions on the product side of Equation 1 possess more disorder than one KNO_3 molecule as a reactant. Finally, the **free energy** change, ΔG, for KNO_3 dissolving in water indicates whether this process occurs spontaneously. If ΔG is negative, solid KNO_3 spontaneously dissolves in water.

We relate the equilibrium constant to the free energy change by Equation 3,

$$\Delta G = -RT \ln K_{sp} \qquad \text{(Eq. 3)}$$

where R is the constant, $8.314 \ J/K \cdot mol$, T is the temperature in kelvins, and $\ln K_{sp}$ is the natural logarithm of the equilibrium constant. Like K_{sp}, the free energy change for a reaction also changes with temperature.

We also relate the free energy change to enthalpy and entropy changes by the Gibbs–Helmholtz equation, Equation 4.

$$\Delta G = \Delta H - T\Delta S \qquad \text{(Eq. 4)}$$

Substituting Equation 3 into Equation 4 yields Equation 5.

$$-RT \ln K_{sp} = \Delta H - T\Delta S \qquad \text{(Eq. 5)}$$

Using algebra, we rearrange the equation into the form for a straight line,

$$y = mx + b$$
$$\ln K_{sp} = -\left(\frac{\Delta H}{R}\right)\left(\frac{1}{T}\right) + \frac{\Delta S}{R} \qquad \text{(Eq. 6)}$$

so that a plot of $\ln K_{sp}$ versus $1/T$ is linear with a slope of $-\Delta H/R$ and a y-intercept of $\Delta S/R$. One assumption in this derivation is that ΔH is a constant, independent of the temperature.

Example 1.

Dissolving 10.1 g of KNO_3 in enough water to make 25.0 mL of solution results in a saturated solution of KNO_3. Determine the K_{sp} for KNO_3.

Let us first calculate the number of moles of KNO_3 that dissolve,

$$10.1g \ KNO_3 \left(\frac{1mol \ KNO_3}{101g \ KNO_3}\right) = 0.100 \ mol \ KNO_3$$

Equation 1 shows that when 0.100 mol KNO_3 dissolves, 0.100 mol K^+ and 0.100 mol NO_3^- form.

We then calculate the concentration of each of these ions in the saturated solution,

$$[K^+] = [NO_3^-] = \left(\frac{0.100 \text{ mol}}{25.0 \text{ mL}}\right)\left(\frac{10^3 \text{ mL}}{1 \text{ L}}\right) = 4.00M$$

According to Equation 2,

$$K_{sp} = [K^+][NO_3^-] = (4.00)(4.00) = 16.0$$

Example 2.

Suppose the equilibrium constant, K_{sp}, for a compound dissolving in water at 25 °C is 2.4. Determine the ΔG for this process at 25 °C.

We apply Equation 3, making sure that the temperature is in the proper units;

$$\Delta G = -(8.314 \text{ J/K} \cdot \text{mol})(25 + 273 \text{ K})(\ln 2.4)$$
$$= -(8.314 \text{ J/K} \cdot \text{mol})(298 \text{ K})(0.88) = -2200 \text{ J/mol}$$

Because ΔG is negative, this compound spontaneously dissolves in water at 25 °C.

Example 3.

Suppose you measure the equilibrium constant, K_{sp}, for a compound dissolving in water at several temperatures, as shown in the following table:

temperature (°C)	K_{sp}
25	2.4
35	3.0
45	3.7

Determine ΔH for this process.

In order to use Equation 6 to determine ΔH, we need to calculate $\ln K_{sp}$ and $1/T$ from the data;

$\frac{1}{T}, K^{-1}$	$\ln K_{sp}$
$\dfrac{1}{(25+273)} = 0.00336$	$\ln 2.4 = 0.88$
$\dfrac{1}{(35+273)} = 0.00325$	$\ln 3.0 = 1.1$
$\dfrac{1}{(45+273)} = 0.00314$	$\ln 3.7 = 1.3$

We plot $\ln K_{sp}$ as a function of $1/T$ and draw the best straight line through the three points:

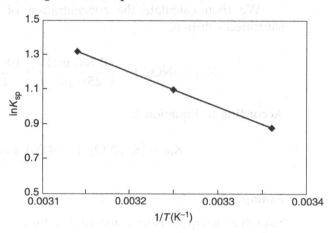

We determine the slope of the line graphically or by regression analysis on a computer spreadsheet:

$$\text{slope} = -2.0 \times 10^3 \text{ K}$$

Finally, we relate the slope of this line to ΔH as shown in Equation 6,

$$\text{slope} = -\frac{\Delta H}{R}, \text{ or upon rearrangment,}$$

$$\Delta H = -R(\text{slope})$$

$$\Delta H = -(8.314 \text{ J/K} \cdot \text{mol})\,(-2.0 \times 10^3 \text{ K})$$

$$= +17000 \text{ J/mol}$$

Because ΔH is positive, this compound absorbs heat from its surroundings to dissolve in water.

Example 4.

The data in Examples 2 and 3 represent the same ionic compound dissolving in water. Determine ΔS for this process at 25 °C.

We know that $\Delta G = -2200$ J/mol at 25 °C (Example 2) and that $\Delta H = 17000$ J/mol (Example 3). Equation 4 relates these three thermodynamic quantities,

$$\Delta G = \Delta H - T\Delta S, \text{ or upon rearrangement,}$$

$$\Delta S = \frac{(\Delta H - \Delta G)}{T}$$

$$\Delta S = \frac{+17000 \text{ J/mol} - (-2200 \text{ J/mol})}{(25 + 273 \text{ K})} = +64 \text{ J/K} \cdot \text{mol}$$

Because ΔS is positive, the products (ions) of the reaction have more disorder than the reactant (the undissolved compound). In this case, the entropy change represents the driving force for the spontaneous dissolution of the compound in water.

Doing this Experiment

At each of several temperatures, you determine the KNO_3 concentration in a saturated solution from the KNO_3 mass and volume of solution. You use these data to calculate the equilibrium constant, K_{sp}, and subsequently the ΔG for the solubility reaction of KNO_3 at each temperature. Furthermore, you plot $\ln K_{sp}$ versus $1/T$ and find the slope of the resulting straight line. Because the slope equals $-\Delta H/R$, you calculate ΔH, which is the heat exchange that accompanies KNO_3 dissolving in water. You use Equation 4 to calculate ΔS from the just-determined values of ΔG and ΔH for this reaction.

PROCEDURE

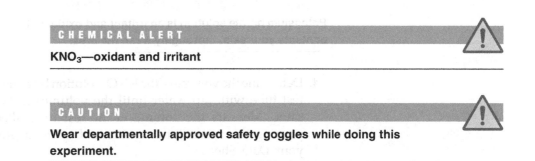

CHEMICAL ALERT

KNO_3—oxidant and irritant

CAUTION

Wear departmentally approved safety goggles while doing this experiment.

1. Assemble a hot-water bath as shown in Figure 1. Set a 400-mL beaker half-filled with tap water on wire gauze on an iron support ring. Place a second ring around the beaker to minimize the possibility of upsetting the water bath.

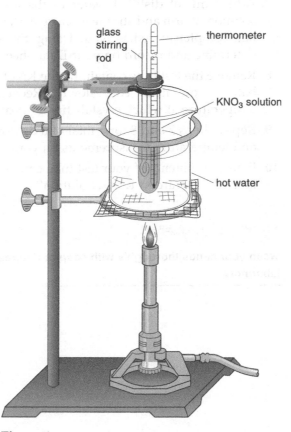

Figure 1

Setup for heating the potassium nitrate solution

2. On a balance, weigh about 20 g of KNO_3 on a tared piece of weighing paper. Record the exact mass of KNO_3 on your Data Sheet. Transfer the KNO_3 to a clean 25×200-mm test tube.

3. Using a graduated cylinder, add 15 mL of distilled or deionized water to the test tube containing the KNO_3. Heat the test tube, as shown in Figure 1, in the assembled hot-water bath. Continue heating, while stirring with a glass stirring rod, until all of the KNO_3 dissolves.

CAUTION

Potassium nitrate solution is an irritant and oxidant. If any of the solution contacts your skin, thoroughly wash the area.

---

4. Determine the volume of the KNO_3 solution by filling another 25×200-mm test tube with tap water until the volumes in both test tubes are the same. Measure the volume in the test tube filled with tap water by pouring this water into a graduated cylinder. Record this volume on your Data Sheet.

5. Remove the test tube with the KNO_3 solution from the hot-water bath and allow it to cool while slowly stirring the solution.

6. Record the temperature when crystals first appear, which is the temperature at which the solid is assumed to be in equilibrium with the solution.

7. Add 5 mL of distilled water to the test tube containing the KNO_3 solution. Warm and stir the mixture in the hot-water bath until the solid has completely redissolved. Using the same method as in Step 4, determine and record on your Data Sheet the solution volume.

8. Remove the test tube containing the KNO_3 solu tion from the hot-water bath. Allow it to cool slowly. Record on your Data Sheet the temperature at which crystals first appear.

9. Repeat Steps 7 and 8 for a total of 6 determinations. Record all volume and temperature measurements on your Data Sheet.

10. Pour the contents of your test tube containing KNO_3 into the container labeled "Discarded KNO_3 Solution".

CAUTION

Wash your hands thoroughly with soap or detergent before leaving the laboratory.

CALCULATIONS

Do the following calculations for each determination and record the results on your Data Sheet.

1. Use the mass of the KNO_3 to calculate the number of moles of KNO_3 present.

2. Use the number of moles of KNO_3 and the volumes you determined at each temperature to calculate the molar concentration of KNO_3 in the solution at each temperature. Because nearly all the KNO_3 is still in solution, its molar concentration equals the molar concentrations of K^+ and of NO_3^- in the saturated solution.

3. Use Equation 2 to calculate the equilibrium constant, K_{sp}, for dissolving KNO_3 in water at each temperature.

4. Convert the temperatures in degrees Celsius (°C) to kelvins (K).

5. Determine the natural logarithm of K_{sp} ($\ln K_{sp}$) at each temperature.

6. Use Equation 3 to calculate ΔG at each temperature.

7. Calculate the reciprocal of each Kelvin temperature, $1/T(K^{-1})$.

8. Using the graph paper provided or a computer spreadsheet program, construct a graph with the y-axis as $\ln K_{sp}$ and the x-axis as $1/T$.

9. Determine the slope of the resulting straight line on this graph by choosing two widely separated points on the line that are not data points and dividing the difference in their y values by the difference in their x values. Alternatively, your laboratory instructor may ask you to use a computer spreadsheet program to perform regression analysis on your experimental data, to plot the data, and to calculate the slope of the best straight line.

10. Calculate ΔH for the reaction. Remember that the slope of the straight line in the $\ln K_{sp}$ versus $1/T$ plot equals $-\Delta H/R$, according to Equation 6.

11. Calculate ΔS at each temperature using Equation 4. Determine the average ΔS. Alternatively, if regression analysis is used, obtain the average ΔS from the y-intercept of the straight line.

_____   _____   _____
Name   *Section*   *Date*

Post-Laboratory Questions

(Use the spaces provided for the answers and additional paper if necessary.)

1. **(a)** Is the process of KNO_3 dissolving in water spontaneous at all temperatures studied? Briefly explain.

   (b) Is the reaction in (a) one that gives off heat or requires heat? Briefly explain.

   (c) Is your value of ΔS consistent with the expected change in disorder for the reaction in Equation 1? Briefly explain.

2. A few compounds exist whose solubility decreases as the temperature increases. How would the values for ΔG, ΔH, and ΔS for these reactions be different from those values observed for the solubility of KNO_3? Briefly explain.

3. (a) What assumption is made about the reaction at the temperature at which crystals become visible?

(b) If this assumption were not true, how would the results for ΔG change?

_____   _____   _____
Name   *Section*   *Date*

Data Sheet

Collecting Data

KNO_3, g   _____

| | determinations | | | | | |
	1	*2*	*3*	*4*	*5*	*6*
total volume, mL	_____	_____	_____	_____	_____	_____
temperature (°C) when crystals form in solution	_____	_____	_____	_____	_____	_____

Determining K_{sp}

number of moles of KNO_3 _____

concentration, $M = [K^+ = [NO_3^-]$	_____	_____	_____	_____	_____	_____
K_{sp}	_____	_____	_____	_____	_____	_____

Determining ΔG

T, K	_____	_____	_____	_____	_____	_____
$\ln K_{sp}$	_____	_____	_____	_____	_____	_____
ΔG, J/mol	_____	_____	_____	_____	_____	_____

Determining ΔH

$1/T$, K^{-1}	_____	_____	_____	_____	_____	_____

slope of the straight line
    defined by $\ln K_{sp}$ versus $1/T$ _____

ΔH, J/mol   _____

Determining ΔS

ΔS, J/K· mol   _____ | _____ | _____ | _____ | _____ | _____

average ΔS, J/K·mol   _____

Calculations:

Name   Section   Date

Pre-Laboratory Assignment

1. What special safety precaution is taken while heating the water bath?

2. What is a saturated solution?

3. Show the algebraic steps used to rearrange Equation 5 to yield Equation 6.

4. When thallium chloride (TlCl) dissolves in water and forms a saturated solution, it establishes the equilibrium:

$$Tl \rightleftharpoons Tl^+(aq) + Cl^-(aq)$$

The solubility of TlCl is 0.29 g in 100 mL of solution at 15.6 °C.

(a) Calculate the molar concentration of Tl^+ and Cl^- in this saturated solution.

(b) Calculate K_{sp} for TlCl at this temperature.

5. Potassium chloride (KCl) dissolves in water and establishes the following equilibrium in a saturated solution:

$$KCl(s) \rightleftharpoons K^+(aq) + Cl^-(aq)$$

The following table supplies information on the solubility of KCl as a function of the Celsius temperature.

temp. (°C)	K_{sp}	T(K)	1/T (k^{-1})	lnK_{sp}	ΔG (J/mol)
20.0	13.3	___	___	___	___
40.0	18.5	___	___	___	___
60.0	24.8	___	___	___	___
80.0	30.5	___	___	___	___

(a) Complete the entries in this table by converting the temperature to kelvins and calculating $1/T$, lnK_{sp}, and ΔG.

(b) Plot lnK_{sp} as a function of $1/T$. Determine the slope of the resulting straight line.

(c) Calculate ΔH for KCl dissolving in water.

(d) Calculate ΔS at 20 °C.

Index

Experimental treatment, 36
Experiments, 28, 35-36, 44, 46, 53, 55
Expertise, 8
exploration, 9, 30, 51
Exposure, 5-6, 9-10, 18, 32
Express, 28, 34, 42
Extended family, 20
extension, 3
External stimuli, 53
External validity, 27, 29
Externalizing, 8, 17
Extinction, 50
Eye contact, 50

F
Fact, 5, 8, 24-26, 33, 35-36, 40, 43
family, 3-4, 11, 13-14, 17-18, 20-22, 24, 29,
    40-41, 44, 46-47, 51, 57
    attachment theory, 51, 57
    genograms, 46
    history, 11, 57
    interventions, 11
    perspectives, 11, 13, 22, 24, 40-41,
        46-47, 57
    single-parent, 17-18
    single-parent families, 17-18
    structure, 17-18, 22, 41, 46-47
    system, 14, 18, 20-21, 24, 46-47, 51, 57
    therapies, 13, 41
    unit, 29
    values, 11, 20-21, 24, 40-41
Family counseling, 46
family lifecycle, 46, 57
Family systems, 46, 57
    approaches, 46
    perspective, 46, 57
FAR, 6, 17
Fear, 5, 17, 49, 52-53
    common, 17
Features, 2, 15, 20, 45
Feedback, 56
Feelings, 5, 16, 28, 30-31, 41-44, 46, 56
Females, 18, 43
Final stage, 23
flexibility, 9, 12-13, 37, 48
focus, 2-3, 7-8, 22-23, 25-27, 31, 42-44, 46,
    48-49, 51, 57
focusing, 41, 43-45
Formal operations, 23
Framing, 2, 24
Freedom, 42
frequency, 34, 53-55
    described, 53
Freud, A., 41
Freud, Sigmund, 41-42
    psychosexual stages, 41
friendship, 8
Frustration, 9, 56
fulfillment, 49
Fusion, 46

G
Gain, 3, 5, 7, 22-25, 27, 29-31, 36-37, 47,
    52, 55
Galton, Francis, 14
Gambling, 54
games, 54
GAP, 21
Gay, 17
Gay men, 17
gender, 7, 16, 33, 43, 45-46, 49
gender identity, 7, 33
Gene expression, 15
Generation Next, 44

Generativity, 44
Genital stage, 42
Genogram, 46
    community, 46
    family, 46
girls, 5, 18, 29, 40, 42
Giving, 11, 35
Global economy, 47
Goals, 10, 20, 42-44, 46, 48, 54-55
    defined, 20
    shaping, 20
    therapy, 43
GOE, 15
goods, 8, 10, 24, 26, 28, 31-32, 37, 41-42,
    54
    defined, 26, 31
    definition, 24
    emergency, 41
    gray, 8
    impulse, 42
Government, 13
Grammar, 12
Gray matter, 8
Great Depression, 11, 20
Group counseling, 44
Groups
    characteristics, 16, 32, 37
    dynamics, 57
    open, 29, 48-49
    roles, 16, 19-20, 44, 49, 56-57
    structured, 3, 29
Growth, 3-4, 9, 13, 15, 22, 44-46
Guilt, 10, 44, 48-49

H
Harmony, 34
Have nots, 3, 36
Health, 4, 18-19, 21, 25, 27, 32, 41, 45, 52
Heart, 12
helping professionals, 8, 24-25, 27
Heterogeneity, 18
Hippocampus, 8, 13
historical eras, 47
History, 11, 33, 45, 57
    19th century, 57
    early, 57
    Middle Ages, 57
    psychiatric, 45
hits, 3
HIV, 36
Homeless
    children, 18
    people, 18
Homeless children, 18
Honesty, 31, 35
hope, 49
household, 18
Human development, 1-3, 6-9, 12-15, 19,
    22, 27, 29, 31-32, 34-36, 39-41,
    44, 50, 52, 56-57
Human nature, 13-14
Hyperactivity, 16, 37

I
Id, 41-42
IDEA, 15, 24, 28, 40-41, 43-47, 49
identification, 25, 38, 44, 49
Identity, 3, 7, 10, 33, 36, 44-49, 52, 57
Identity development, 45-46, 48-49, 57
Identity versus role confusion, 10
Illustrations, 21-22
Image, 22
Impact, 3-4, 9, 18-19, 45-46, 52
Impasse, 46

impulsivity, 16
income, 17-18
Independent variable, 27, 32
India, 8
Individual Psychology, 43
individualism, 19, 21
Individuation, 43
Industrial Revolution, 40, 57
Infancy, 3, 6, 9, 44
Influence
    process, 4, 11, 13, 19-20, 24, 55-57
    psychological, 4, 8, 35, 55-56
    social, 4, 7, 11, 17-18, 20-21, 24, 55-57
information, 5-6, 12-13, 16, 28-31, 34-37,
    44, 48, 50
    in-depth, 29
Informed consent, 35-38
Initiative, 44
Innovation, 2
Insight, 31, 41-43
Institutions, 20
Instrumental conditioning, 53
Instruments, 28, 30, 34, 37
Insurance, 2
Integration, 43, 49
Integrity, 36, 38, 44-45
intellectual resources, 9
intelligence, 8, 14, 16, 27
Interaction, 4-5, 13-17, 19-21, 28, 34, 38,
    43-46, 48, 50, 52, 57
Interaction effect, 16
interdependence, 7, 14, 45
Interest, 29, 32, 35, 43
Internal environment, 13
Internal validity, 27, 29
Internalization, 6, 48-49
Internalizing, 17
International
    UNICEF, 41
Interpretation, 12, 28
intervention, 11, 25, 27, 38, 49, 54-55
    defined, 25
    family, 11
interviews, 29-30
    structured, 29-30
intimacy, 44
Intimate partner violence, 9, 17
intimates, 3, 9, 17, 44
introductions, 39-40
Introjection, 42, 45
IQ, 18
Isolation, 18, 29-30, 44
Israel, 17
Italy, 8

J
Japan, 34
    population, 34
Japanese culture, 34
job, 8, 20, 25, 47
Jung, Carl, 43, 57

K
Kenya, 8
Knowledge, 1-2, 5, 7-9, 12-13, 15, 19, 22,
    24-27, 29, 35-38, 40
    requirements, 36

L
labeling, 26
labels, 26
language, 3, 12, 14, 18-19, 22-24, 29-30, 33,
    49, 52
    emotional, 18, 52